GW00385617

# The
# science of human
# progress

# The
# science of human
# progress

*by*

ROBIN HOLLIDAY

*The discovery of the molecular basis of life has produced a
revolution in science which could lead both to a complete
understanding of the biological nature of man and the
solution of many of the problems of human societies*

OXFORD
OXFORD UNIVERSITY PRESS
NEW YORK · TORONTO
1981

Oxford University Press, Walton Street, Oxford OX2 6DP
London Glasgow New York Toronto
Delhi Bombay Calcutta Madras Karachi
Kuala Lumpur Singapore Hong Kong Tokyo
Nairobi Dar Es Salaam Cape Town
Melbourne Wellington

and associate companies in
Beirut Berlin Ibadan Mexico City

Published in the United States
by Oxford University Press, New York

© Robin Holliday 1981

All rights reserved. No part of this publication may be reproduced,
stored in a retrieval system, or transmitted, in any form or by any means,
electronic, mechanical, photocopying, recording, or otherwise, without
the prior permission of Oxford University Press

This book is sold subject to the condition that it shall not, by way
of trade or otherwise, be lent, re-sold, hired or otherwise circulated
without the publisher's prior consent in any form of binding or cover
other than that in which it is published and without a similar condition
including this condition being imposed on the subsequent purchaser

British Library Cataloguing in Publication Data
Holliday, Robin
The science of human progress.
1. Biology
I. Title
574      QH307.2      80–41353
ISBN 0–19–854711–0

Filmset in Monophoto by Latimer Trend & Company Ltd, Plymouth
Printed in Great Britain by
Lowe & Brydone Printers Limited, Thetford, Norfolk

# Preface

THIS book is about the future of biological science. Unlike some others which have recently been published, it presents an optimistic view. Many people now realize that a revolution in the study of biology at the molecular level has occurred in the last twenty-five years or so, but the way this will affect human lives and human society is controversial. Much of the recent discussion has been related to the development of biotechnology or genetic engineering in the not too distant future. I am looking much further ahead than that; in particular, at the possible consequences the extraordinary success of the methods of molecular biology will have for the study of man himself. Not only will it lead to a much fuller understanding of the structure and function of his body, including his brain, but also his behaviour and the way he interacts with other human beings. I argue that this can only help to solve many of the problems man is faced with today, including above all his ability to destroy himself with nuclear weapons. The original title for this book was *The race*: to save the human race we must win the race between self-knowledge and self-destruction.

My approach will be regarded by many readers as naïve, over simplistic, or even old-fashioned. In the latter part of the last century and the early decades of this one, there was a spirit of optimism about biological research. It was felt that the consequences of obtaining knowledge about the living world could only be beneficial to man in the future. Many eminent scientists and writers, including T. S. Huxley, H. G. Wells, J. S. Huxley, J. B. S. Haldane, L. Hogben, and J. D. Bernal, believed it was part of their professional duty to explain the new knowledge to non-scientists. Educated laymen, for their part, kept themselves reasonably well informed about a variety of new areas of biology. The situation is different today. On the whole, molecular biologists feel that their field of study is too complex and sophisticated to explain to people who do not already have a scientific training. Non-scientists are quite out of touch with what is really going on in modern laboratories, in spite of the efforts of television and radio to transmit some of this information. Moreover, there is widespread suspicion of scientists; it is often felt that their work is sinister and could lead to dangerous consequences rather than beneficial ones. Because there are now many examples of the damaging effects of scientific research (or, more accurately, the subsequent technology), the spirit of optimism has all too often been replaced by one of pessimism or hostility.

This book is intended to counteract that view but, more important, it attempts to provide positive reasons for *the necessity* of the pursuit of biological knowledge at the fundamental level. In addition it embodies a plea for rationalism, which must necessarily go along with an acceptance of the overwhelming evidence we now have about the very nature of life itself. Nowadays it is common to sneer at rational attitudes and it is fashionable to believe that there are all manner of strange phenomena in the universe which are outside or beyond explanation by scientific investigation. Also, many non-scientists who consider themselves to be generally well informed are often proud of their lack of knowledge of science.

I have three categories of reader in mind. First, scientists themselves, simply because their assessment of the value of their own work does vary so widely. I hope that this book will inject a feeling of optimism in an area of discussion which is all too often plagued by self-doubt and self-criticism. Second, non-scientists who are interested in science, but who frequently have difficulty in understanding what has been achieved and are therefore often misled by some of the more lurid scenarios which portray the scientist as the harbinger of evil. Third, those who are responsible for science policy, and the provision and administration of support for research laboratories. Fifty years ago, financial support for research was very limited, but in general scientists could pursue the work they wished to do. Since the last war, financial support has grown enormously, but in recent years more and more pressure has been put on scientists to adopt research programmes which are likely to be of practical benefit in the reasonably near future. As far as biological research is concerned, I believe the policy-makers cannot see the wood for the trees, because they have missed altogether the possibility of the most important benefits that science could bestow on mankind.

This book is not intended to be a work of scholarship and I have deliberately kept references to source material to a minimum. I shall be criticized for straying outside my own professional field of biological research and I should apologize in advance to any authors whose views I have restated, or perhaps misrepresented, without citing their publications. Among the writings of contemporary biologists, I have been most influenced and impressed by *Molecules and men* by Francis Crick;[1] *Chance and necessity* by the late Jaques Monod;[2] and essays in *The art of the soluble*[3] and *The hope of progress*[4] by Sir Peter Medawar. I must also acknowledge the influence of the late Norwood Russell Hanson, who was an enthusiastic and illuminating teacher of the philosophy of science at the University of Cambridge. Chapter 2 is a distillation of everything I learned from him more than twenty years ago. I am greatly indebted to Alison Flood, Tom Kirkwood, Nicholas Parsons, and Antonia Cowan for encouraging me to write the book. They also provided valuable comments, and criticisms of the first draft, as did many others, including John Fincham, John Menninger, Harman Sumray, Michael Evans, Jonathan Cooke, Janet Dickson, John Holliday, Lily Huschtscha, Robert Moore, and Diana Holliday. I also thank Rita Harris, Freda Oates, and Rita Findon, who could always find time to type chapters in various stages of preparation. I am particularly grateful to Christopher and Hilary Finzi for allowing me to stay and write in peace and seclusion at their house in Sanissac, France. Finally, I must thank Sir Arnold Burgen and the Medical Research Council for granting the study leave which made it possible for me to complete this book.

*Berkhamsted*
*March* 1980                                                      R.H.

# Contents

# 1. Introduction

It is simply not worth arguing with anyone so obtuse as
not to realise that this complex of discoveries is the greatest
achievement of science in the twentieth century.
> P. B. Medawar on molecular biology[1]

In the first forty or so years of this century a revolution in
physics occurred which led to an understanding of the structure
of atoms and of the means by which energy could be released
from them. This research was carried out by scientists of the
highest intellectual calibre who were, for the most part, concerned solely with the pursuit of knowledge for its own sake.
This knowledge was subsequently applied in the construction
of nuclear weapons of mass destruction.

In the past twenty-five years, a revolution in biology has
occurred. At the beginning of this period it could not have been
foreseen just how successful the study of the basic processes of
life at the molecular level would be. The speed of advance of
knowledge in this field of molecular biology has been astonish-
ing and there is at present no sign that it is slowing down. It is
very hard to believe that the unravelling of the main features of
life at the molecular level will not be of the greatest significance
and importance for mankind, and no one has made the point
more forcefully than Medawar in the quotation above. The
problem is to decide just why molecular biology is important
and to try to understand what significance it has for society in
general.

Molecular biology arose under the shadow of nuclear physics,
and the informed and the uninformed public cannot be blamed
for making comparisons between the two scientific revolutions.
The argument is that nuclear physicists carried out fundamental research without realizing that the knowledge they
gained would be applied in the way it has. Similarly molecular
biologists pursue in greater and greater depth the genetic
structure of living organisms and have developed the means to
manipulate genetic material, or other basic components of life,
in the laboratory. The common conclusion is that in the end

...₀ will lead to a sinister biological technology which may, in one way or another, be used for evil purposes. This view is one of the reasons for the current widespread suspicion of science in general and overt hostility to molecular genetics in particular.

I do not know of any sound argument or any logical basis for a direct comparison between the possible consequences of research in nuclear physics and molecular biology. On the contrary, I shall develop the argument in this book that the further pursuit of molecular biology is of vital importance for the future wellbeing of mankind. It has become a cliché to say that man's ability to manipulate his environment or create a potentially self-destructive technology has far outstripped his capacity for moral advance. Everywhere we see the over-whelming evidence that science is an extraordinarily successful way of obtaining new knowledge, and yet everywhere we see the same patterns of human behaviour which have existed for centuries. Nevertheless, I believe that the common view that science cannot and never will contribute to man's moral or 'spiritual' development is false. I try to justify my belief in this book.

In unfolding the argument I shall first briefly review later in this chapter the position of the scientist in society at the present time. One of the major problems is that of communication between scientists and non-scientists. This is in part due to a widespread ignorance of the underlying reasons for the success scientists have in acquiring new knowledge. I therefore outline the nature of the scientific method in Chapter 2 and try to explain just why it is so successful. In the following chapter I review the background of molecular biology and some of the most important advances which have occurred in this field. This is intended to be comprehensible to non-scientists and my hope is that it will show just how much fundamental knowledge has been gained about the very nature of life itself, namely the chemical structure of the genetic material, the way genes are transmitted from generation to generation, and the mechanism by which they transmit their information—via the genetic code—to the components which make up the structure of all cells, tissues, and organisms. Superlatives are frowned on in scientific circles, but it should be fully understood that mole-cular biology is not just the consequence of efficient scientists working away in their laboratories, but represents one of the peaks of all human intellectual activity. Everyone understands the implications of the atomic age, but the same is not yet true of 'the molecular age', which is now upon us.

The great unifying principle in all biology is Darwinian natural selection. The structure and function of all organisms, including man, can be fully understood only in terms of their evolutionary origins. I therefore provide an outline of the main principles of natural selection in Chapter 4. The key to the success of molecular biology is that it knits together into a cohesive whole a variety of experimental approaches, particularly genetics, biochemistry, biophysics, and cell biology. It has already become dominant in fields of research such as immunology, virology, or developmental biology. I predict in Chapter 5 that spectacular advances will be made in our understanding of the way complex organisms develop and coordinate the activity of their various body tissues. The great challenge is to understand the way the central nervous system is put together and carries out all its complex functions, but the ultimate challenge is to understand the structure and function of the human brain itself. I do not believe this understanding is beyond the reach of scientific investigation, although it may take a very long time to achieve this goal.

At this point I should make clear that my approach will be labelled by some readers as 'reductionist'. This term is usually used in a derogatory sense by 'anti-reductionists' who believe that an organism is something more than the sum of its molecular components. It is not clear to me, or to many other molecular biologists, quite what anti-reductionists actually believe. It is true that if a complex machine, such as a motor car, is first taken apart into all its component parts, one would not then discern how the machine works. But to understand how it does work, one needs to know something about the laws of physics and chemistry, what the component parts are and how they all interact with each other. In one sense the machine is more than the sum of its components, but in another it is not. The argument therefore is simply about words and definitions. Molecular biologists have shown that organisms are made up of complex molecules. How all these interact with each other in plants and animals is the basic problem for the future.

Organisms can of course be understood at various levels, without looking at molecules, but a complete understanding will necessarily require a study of molecular components. Everyone is interested in human behaviour. This is shown by the widespread study of psychology and sociology and the generally accepted view that these are fields of research which can be understood by non-specialists. More recently, there has been a vogue in applying some of the well-established principles of animal behaviour to human behaviour. The controversial new field of sociobiology is the most ambitious of all, since it attempts to provide a more biological basis for the more traditional human sciences of psychology and sociology.[2] To do this it takes into account the evolutionary forces which allowed man to emerge by natural selection from his primate ancestors, and it extrapolates from known examples of the genetic basis of animal behaviour to emphasize the importance of genetic influences on human behaviour. I shall return to the field of human behaviour in Chapter 8. Although existing approaches may yield some new information, I believe that progress will inevitably be limited when so little is known about brain function. I shall review some of the enormous gaps in our knowledge of the biological nature of man and argue that these gaps will eventually be filled by a much more profound study of memory, perception, the process of thought, and language, all of which will depend on an understanding of the central nervous system at the molecular, cellular, and physiological levels. When we obtain concrete information about the basis of human behaviour, human societies will be transformed. I believe that it may then become possible to define solutions to innumerable problems which face man today, not least his propensity to destroy himself by resorting to war. In 1966 Francis Crick, the leading molecular biologist of his generation, put it this way:

It can be confidently stated that our present knowledge of the brain is so primitive—approximately at the stage of the four humours in medicine or of bleeding in therapy (what is psychoanalysis but mental bleeding?)—that when we do have fuller knowledge our whole picture of ourselves is bound to change radically. Much that is now culturally acceptable will then seem to be nonsense. People with training in the arts still feel that in spite of the alterations made in their life by technology—by the internal combustion engine, by penicillin, by the Bomb—modern science has little to do with what concerns them most deeply. As far as today's science is concerned this is partly true, but tomorrow's science is going to knock their culture right out from under them.[3]

It goes without saying that the availability of knowledge and information does not ensure that it will be used. However, in Chapter 7 I cite various examples in the field of biomedicine, where knowledge has been made available, has been accepted by the public, and has had very beneficial consequences. The machinery for disseminating the medical information which is obtained in research laboratories to the public at large is reasonably successful, perhaps because people are usually very interested in and concerned about the health of their bodies. In many cases patients or their relatives have to make choices between this or that course of action. I try to show that when they are given the basic information, people make sensible decisions much more often than not, and this does not depend on any detailed knowledge of the underlying science. It often simply becomes self-evident that a particular choice should be made. In some cases a moral judgement is also involved. People are also very interested in normal and abnormal patterns of the behaviour of individuals and also in all manner of social problems. When information becomes available in these fields, I believe it will also be acted upon. Scientists will be instrumental in obtaining this knowledge, but it is up to the general public to decide how it should be used.

Let me now return to the role of science and scientists in society today and in the immediate past. Traditionally, fundamental research was an academic discipline: the pursuit of natural knowledge for its own sake was a perfectly acceptable justification for scientists' work. This view was certainly the dominant one up until the end of the nineteenth century and was very widely accepted in the first few decades of this century. Nowadays attitudes have changed substantially, largely because it is realized that fundamental research can lead to technological applications which can be either harmful or beneficial. The organizations which support scientific research, and particularly those which ultimately draw their funds from the taxpayer, have tended to regard pure academic research as an unnecessary luxury and have emphasized the need to pursue particular goals which will be, or are likely to be, of benefit to the community at large. The current pursuit of 'mission-oriented' research is not just restricted to Britain, it is a world-wide phenomenon. The public approves of this policy because by and large it is believed that science advances because laboratories are built and equipped and scientists are trained and installed in them. There is little realization that progress in a particular field, such as cancer research, critically depends on creative insight and original ideas and that these will not necessarily arise as a consequence of setting up well-manned and well-equipped laboratories. Brain power is all too often the limiting factor in scientific research.

It is true that molecular biology is the direct result of funda-mental research, but the general belief of scientists themselves, and most particularly of those who provide financial and other support for scientific research, is that an understanding of the molecular composition and function of living organisms is justified because it will necessarily lead to beneficial advances in the medical and agricultural sciences in the foreseeable future. For example, the basis of cancer will be understood and cures or effective preventative treatments will be devised. The biochemical defect in inherited diseases will be uncovered in more and more cases and this will inevitably lead to ways and means of removing the deleterious symptoms. Plants will be bred which can obtain their nitrogen directly from the air rather than from fertilizers. It is not at all difficult to imagine a very large number of similar practical benefits which will result from further research in molecular biology and related fields.

Although many biologists are quite content to accept this justification for their work, some certainly realize that science does not proceed just because governments or other bodies set up laboratories and provide jobs for scientists. These scientists understand that their motives are not altruistic, but instead, rather selfish. Successful scientific research is extremely satis-fying and enjoyable. The driving force in the laboratory is indeed in many cases the pursuit of knowledge for its own sake. It is often the pioneers in experiment, the originators of new theories, who are most aware of the fact that their work is *not* stimulated by the possibility of future benefits. Rather, their creative urge is intrinsic to themselves, and can be just as exciting as creative activity in the fields of literature, painting, and music. We should, however, notice a fundamental difference between the creative artist and the creative scientist. The successful product of the writer, painter, or composer will be shared or enjoyed by other people. The artist may also be selfish, but he is using particular means to express his feelings, and the medium used allows them to be communicated to people who are receptive. Science can also be communicated to other people, but not for the same reason. It is true that scientists often describe experiments by others as 'beautiful' or 'elegant', but it is arguable whether any aesthetic pleasure is involved; rather, the scientist admires the skill, insight, or technique which has been used. Moreover, scientists are mainly interested in the work of others only in so far as it relates to their own work. (Since enormous numbers of papers are published each year in scientific journals, it is often a relief for a research scientist to scan a journal in his own field and find that there is no contribution he need read, because none is relevant to his own work! The walking encyclopaedia, the scientist who collects information from the scientific literature for its own sake, is increasingly uncommon, perhaps because there is usually pressure on him to produce and publish his own experimental results.)

We thus reach a dilemma. The average scientist in a university or institute is expected to carry out research which his employers believe will be of ultimate benefit to society. Yet he is not always in a position to see what that benefit might actually be; in his day-to-day work he is indulging himself in a creative activity which is certainly more enjoyable than many other professional occupations. The knowledge and information gained gives him satisfaction, but in itself it does not provide much satisfaction for other people.

The realization that this is the case has had profound consequences for scientists. It has led to a great deal of soul-searching and the setting-up in recent years of organizations or groups to examine the social responsibility of scientists. There has been a great deal of discussion and argument, but little consensus of opinion. Molecular biologists have disagreed about the possible hazards of the genetic manipulation of DNA (a topic I shall discuss in Chapter 6). Some scientists have changed fields, moving into areas which seem more socially relevant;

for example, research into the biological effects of man-made chemicals in the environment. Many justify their work because they realize there is a strong element of chance in scientific research, that is, it cannot be predicted which group might be successful. The money spent is fully justified because the occasional breakthrough (such as the discovery of penicillin) will be so beneficial that it will easily justify the support of many other laboratories which have not been so productive. Others seem to believe simply that society owes them a living, because they were trained for a particular type of job at a university and it is not for them to question the purpose or value of what they are actually doing. If jobs are not available, they may become disillusioned and leave science altogether, rather than adapting themselves to economic realities by moving into a related area of research where there is more demand for scientists.

In this book I am trying to redefine the role of biologists in society. They are in a privileged position not only because they are paid to do work which they enjoy, but also because they are instrumental in acquiring new information which will add to the overall body of scientific knowledge and can be drawn on by subsequent generations of scientists. I am not returning to the traditional view by arguing that the acquisition of knowledge for its own sake is a sufficient justification for scientific research, but I do argue that fundamental research now will be of fundamental importance to society in the future. Much time and effort is spent on mission-oriented research of indifferent quality, which in many cases leads nowhere. Much more should be devoted to basic research of very high quality, particularly in those fields of biology which have proved to be so successful in the last twenty-five years. I maintain that the knowledge which will be gained will ultimately be of un-dreamed of benefit to man, because it will help solve many of the problems societies are faced with today.

# 2. The success of the scientific method

I believe there is at least one philosophical problem in which all thinking men are interested. It is the problem of cosmology: the problem of understanding the world—including ourselves and our knowledge, as part of the world. All science is cosmology, I believe, and for me the interest of philosophy lies solely in the contributions which it has made to it.

K. R. Popper[1]

IN this chapter I shall discuss two problems which should be the concern of scientists and non-scientists alike and attempt to show how they are interrelated. One is the problem of the logical basis of the methods used by scientists in their everyday work and the other is the problem of communication between scientists and non-scientists.

No one can dispute the fact that the methods scientists use provide an extraordinarily successful means of obtaining new information, or what I shall often refer to as exact knowledge, about both the physical and biological world. Since science is so successful it might be assumed that an essential part of any scientist's training would be a study of the logical procedures, or the underlying philosophy, of the scientific method itself. As P. B. Medawar has pointed out, nothing could be further from the truth.[2] Scientists hardly ever receive formal training in the theoretical or logical basis of the scientific method and most remain ignorant by choice. It is an open question whether or not this has any serious effect on the quality of their research. It has been left largely to philosophers to worry about the procedures scientists actually use and to try to understand just why science is as successful as it is.

On the other hand, scientists are certainly very well aware of the problems of communication with laymen or non-scientists. There is not only the difficulty of explaining what they are doing in non-technical language, but even more important, the non-scientist has no easy way of judging whether the scientists' conclusions are justified and likely to be correct. This

9

problem gets more and more severe as the sophistication of science increases. There is no easy way of solving it, but I believe it is essential to both the scientist and non-scientist who may be trying to communicate with each other to have some solid appreciation of the general procedures which are used to obtain exact knowledge. I shall therefore first review the conventional interpretation of the logical basis of the scientific method. Later on I shall briefly discuss an alternative to the conventional interpretation which has been elaborated by the philosopher Karl R. Popper.

One type of reasoning used in science is the *deductive* procedure. Starting with axioms or premises which are taken to be self-evident, one can deduce step by step the logical consequences. Mathematics is based on deduction and an example which is often used to illustrate this is Euclidian geometry. Euclid started with simple self-evident axioms; for example, that a straight line is the shortest distance between two points. He derived a series of important conclusions which are far from self-evident. It is not at all obvious, for example, that the sum of the internal angles of any triangle invariably add up to two right-angles. But Euclid demonstrates logically that this must be so if the truth of the axioms is accepted. The limitation of the method is to establish the truth of the axioms. If space is curved rather than linear, as Euclid assumed it to be, then a straight line is not necessarily the shortest distance between two points. In non-linear space it is difficult to know what a straight line really is. Suppose Euclid wanted to test his conclusions by empirical observation. The angles of accurately drawn triangles would indeed add up to two right-angles, but now imagine a very large triangle made up in the following way. Three points are selected at the edge of a large lake and they are joined by three taut, floating ropes. Now when the three angles are measured they would be slightly greater than two right-angles, since the surface of the lake follows the curvature of the earth. In fact, the truth of axioms can never be assumed, so deductive reasoning alone is always inadequate. Indeed, the whole field of pure mathematics is an abstraction which provides us with no *real* information about the world or the universe. Nevertheless, deductive reasoning is a vital component of the scientific method.

The problem then is to establish the truth of axioms. This involves observation or measurement and is where the vital importance of experimental procedures becomes apparent. Unfortunately it is also the point where the logical problems of the scientific method also become apparent. The conventional view is that the truth of axioms can be established by *inductive* procedures. An example can be provided from the work of Galileo, who was the first true exponent of the experimental method. Galileo measured with fair accuracy the rate of acceleration of objects under the influence of gravity. One experimental procedure involved rolling a ball down an inclined plane and measuring the time it took to travel certain distances. On every occasion measured the ball took the same length of time to travel any particular distance, and Galileo concluded that it would always take the same length of time. From observations like this he was able by deductive methods to formulate precisely important properties of the force of gravitation. But the assumption that the ball would *always* take the same time to travel a given distance is not logically valid. It is conceivable that the atoms in the air in front of the ball might for an instant move in a contrary direction, thus slowing down its acceleration. More important, how could Galileo be so sure that the gravitational force was constant? Suppose it varied at certain times, but he did not happen to make his measurements at these times? Of course Galileo's work was completely correct, because the probability of atoms in the air moving non-randomly is extremely remote and gravitation does not vary with time. (That this must be so became clear later on when the relationship between the planetary orbits and gravitation was worked out.) Nevertheless the principle of drawing conclusions from a limited number of observations—the principle of simple enumeration—is logically false. It has been a continual worry to philosophers that the method of experimental science, which is demonstrably successful, is based on illogical procedures. The central problem is that when a scientist is entering a new area of investigation, it is not at all clear that a limited number of observations can possibly establish a universal principle or 'law of nature'.

Let us for the moment leave aside the concern of the philosophers and examine in more detail what exactly happens in real situations. In the first place, inductive reasoning in science is closely analogous to what occurs in everyday experience. Our lives would be impossible to lead if we could not rely on the principle of induction or simple enumeration. For instance, we cannot be logically sure that the sun will rise tomorrow, but we would be driven mad if we worried about it not rising. Nor when we visit a local shopping centre do we imagine that the grocer or the bank we wish to visit will have unaccountably closed or disappeared. If we know there is a factory producing cars, we can assume that most of them coming off the production line will actually work. If, say, one in a thousand is defective, this does not affect the conclusion that the factory does indeed produce functional cars. In the area of natural science, we can say that all giraffes have long necks, although we might find an occasional defective giraffe with a short neck. Or, if we found a population of giraffes with short necks, we would probably give them another name, so they would not in fact be giraffes according to our initial definition.

These examples make a basic point, but they are essentially trivial, so let us now consider one which has a much more realistic bearing on the way biological research is actually carried out. Gregor Mendel selected a number of varieties of the garden pea which had distinct characteristics and in breeding experiments he studied the transmission of these characteristics to offspring. From a combination of experiment, observation, and deduction he discovered the basic rules governing the inheritance and segregation of genetic factors (which we now call genes). However, this was in only one species and Mendel clearly wanted to generalize his discoveries to others. He chose the plant *Hieracium*, but unfortunately what he did not know was that this plant has a non-sexual (or apomictic) system for producing seeds. For this reason he was quite unable to obtain the same results that he had with the pea. This must have been very discouraging and perhaps led him to think that he had not after all discovered the basic laws of genetics. No doubt he was aware of the logical fallacy of forming general conclusions from a limited number of observations. In any event he made little attempt to communicate his results to others or to continue his research. Thirty years later his work was rediscovered by three scientists independently and soon after a large number of breeding experiments with both plants and animals were carried out. In almost every case Mendel's conclusions from the experiments with peas were confirmed. Not even philosophers should now be hesitant about making the generalization that genes in organisms *are* inherited according to Mendel's laws. Notice that we do not have to study every species to make this generalization. We do not need to study the genetics of the elephant (which in any case would be hard to do) to be as sure as makes no difference that it too transmits its genetic material from generation to generation in exactly the same way. Of course there are some species (and *Hieracium* is one) which have developed alternative breeding systems, but these are interesting exceptions to a general rule.

The example of the origins of genetics also illustrates another aspect of the scientific method. Reading Mendel's paper today, one is astounded by the originality of his experimental approach, the skill with which he analysed his results, and the insight which led him to the correct conclusions.[3] He is regarded as the founder of genetics, but notice that it did not really become a science until many of the other experiments had been done with a variety of species. Obviously none of the investigations which confirmed his results were as important as his, but they were playing a crucial part in establishing the validity of Mendel's laws. The example clearly illustrates the way in which scientific research actually advances. Scientists with particular insight form a vanguard. Their important observations or theories start a 'bandwagon' of further investigations usually by less original scientists. These further studies will either establish the general validity of the first observation or they may show that different results are obtained with other experimental systems. Or they may demonstrate that the first experiments were actually incorrect.

Scientists frequently complain that there are too many scientific journals containing detailed reports (or papers, as they are usually called) of boring, repetitive, or pedantic observations. This is quite true; but most of the observations are providing further evidence for one or another part of the particular branch of science concerned. What in fact happens is that the probability that the general conclusions are correct increases with the number of confirmatory observations. (A scientist in a particular field does not have to keep in his head all the details of these observations; but he is generally aware that they exist and he can always go and check the results of any investigation in the appropriate journal or book.)

Another aspect of scientific research which is vital to its success is that it is objective, impersonal, and international. Any scientist who carries out experiments and publishes the results always provides the details of the actual laboratory techniques which were used. Thus any other scientist can repeat the experiment in exactly the same way if he wishes to do so. There is therefore a built-in safeguard against dishonesty or cheating. If any scientist has fabricated results, he is invariably exposed sooner or later, unless of course the work is so unimportant that no one is interested in repeating it. Science is a communal activity in the sense that laboratories in different parts of the world are carrying out related work and they interact synergistically. The interaction may be collaborative, or it may be competitive. The latter situation certainly acts as a stimulus to research, and the duplication of an experimental programme, for reasons I have explained, will reinforce the overall validity of the results. It rarely makes sense for any one country to set up a laboratory or institute to tackle one specific problem in isolation. The chances are, if the subject is important enough, that there will be other similar laboratories in other countries. Governments or other bodies which support scientists sometimes seem to be unaware of the thoroughly international character of most basic research since they are frequently concerned only with a national science policy. They may also be misled by influential individual scientists who have opinions which are at variance with the scientific community at large in a particular area of research. Such scientists may of course be pioneers with creative vision, but unfortunately they are rather more likely to be out of date or out of touch with the body of work other scientists are carrying out.

The work of Galileo and Mendel illustrates the vital importance of a combination of observation and deductive reasoning. Mere observation, or the collection of facts, does not lead one very far. It is essential to make predictions by deductive reasoning and test these by further observation. It is often the case in science that the formulation of hypotheses and the making of predictions requires a degree of intuition or creative insight which is so rare that it is the limiting factor in advancing a field of research. A theory is of course of value only if it makes predictions which can be tested by observation and experiment. If the prediction is very unusual, perhaps quite contrary to traditional expectation, a single valid observation may be sufficient to confirm it. A famous example was Albert Einstein's prediction that light should bend under the influence of gravity, which was confirmed by observations made during the few minutes of a solar eclipse. Science is built up of a superstructure of interrelated hypotheses which lead to predictions and then to further observations. Each stage increases the overall corpus of knowledge and makes it less and less likely that the foundations of that particular branch of science are based on false axioms or invalid premises.

A pyramid provides a convenient image of the structure of a science. The apex represents the most recent theories and experiments. One possibility is that they may turn out to be wrong and the apex is then removed and eventually replaced by another. It is impossible to increase the height of the pyramid without making many supporting observations, in other words by strengthening the foundations. The larger the structure becomes the less easy it is to undermine it. It achieves a permanence which is immovable. A common misconception about science is that a traditional or conventional scientific interpretation can be completely overthrown by a new discovery or a new way of thinking about existing observations. Thus it is often stated that Einstein 'proved' that the Newtonian picture of the universe was incorrect. What Newton did in fact was to provide an extremely accurate description of the properties of gravitation and motion which for most practical purposes is perfectly adequate today.[4] Einstein showed that Newton did not provide a complete description and that there were additional possibilities to be taken into account. He produced a more accurate or valid concept of motion and gravity which makes more accurate predictions than does Newton's.

In biology it would be inconceivable to imagine observations which would make Mendelian genetics invalid, although many of the details or finer subtleties underlying the transmission of genes from generation to generation are continually being discovered. The molecular basis of the genetic code has now been unravelled (see Chapter 3) and has been found to be the same in bacteria, man, and many other organisms. It is now inconceivable that the basic discovery could be wrong, or that the code could suddenly change since it must have been in existence for a thousand million years or more, but to be convinced of these strong statements requires knowledge of the experimental evidence. Nevertheless, new organisms might be discovered which use a slightly different version of the genetic code.

Now we are in a better position to understand the problem of communication between scientist and non-scientist. The person who has spent many years acquainting himself with, or becoming aware of, the experimental observations may be readily convinced of the validity of conclusions which are drawn from those observations. However, someone who has very little knowledge of the observations may not be convinced at all by the conclusions. In the physical sciences, most people unaware of the evidence are quite willing to accept the conclusions of scientists, but this is far from true in biology. One reason for this is that the conclusions impinge much more on religious or other traditional views about the origin, purpose, or destiny of human beings. Thus geneticists who study the structure of populations of animals and plants in natural environments are almost unanimous in accepting the view that such species evolved by Darwinian natural selection (see Chapter 4). Other biologists usually accept this too, but perhaps with less conviction. Non-biologists, however, frequently dispute or disagree with the conclusion that evolution has occurred by natural selection. Unfortunately there is no easy way of solving the problem. The layman who asks the question 'Can you be absolutely sure that your conclusions are correct?' can only be given the answer that they are very likely, or perhaps almost certain, to be correct. Unfortunately there is often an element of doubt which to the scientist may be only a remote possibility, but which is sufficient for the layman to justify the rejection of a conclusion he would prefer not to believe. Persuasion depends on spelling out the evidence—the numerous observations which are available—but in practice this is almost always impossible to do. I mentioned earlier that many of the observations of everyday life are not, in principle, any different from those of scientists. People are convinced the sun will rise tomorrow because it is simply common experience that it will do so. They do expect order and they do make simple predictions which will be fulfilled (for example, the times when their bank will be open or closed). When they move into an area with which they are not familiar, such as biological science, they can easily make nonsensical remarks or criticisms. One example will illustrate the point. The well-known newspaper columnist Katherine Whitehorn wrote an article in *The Observer*[5] on the possible relationship between the intelligence of parents and their children, which included the sentence: 'This is as good a time as any, too, to point out that the monk, Mendel, who worked out with his pea-plants the principle of "one black and one white and two khaki" is now widely considered to have cooked his results.' The implication is that all Mendelian genetics has been discredited. This type of nonsensical comment can unfortunately be put about by supposedly well-informed people and read by tens of thousands of others. It is the formal equivalent of maintaining that the sun will *not* rise tomorrow.

To avoid this situation it is essential for the non-scientist to understand the general structure of science, the way it is studied and the way in which it advances. If the majority of scientists who are knowledgeable about a given field agree about a certain conclusion, the layman cannot do better than accept this. If, however, a single scientist reaches a conclusion on his own, the non-scientist should be suspicious. Scientists with eccentric views may sometimes turn out to be right, but more often they are wrong. It is unfortunate that individuals of this type often vehemently propagate their own views and may seriously mislead the general public. This is also true of certain serious and influential writers, such as Arthur Koestler, who can disagree with the conclusions of scientists by ignoring the mass of experimental evidence.[6]

Scientists are frequently accused of being unnecessarily sceptical about the validity of unusual happenings or phenomena which are thought to be outside the domain of science. Consider the specific example of Uri Geller's claim to bend metallic objects without the application of any apparent force. It is clear that many people are willing to accept that there are unknown forces which Geller has somehow harnessed and of which scientists are unaware. There is, however, a vast knowledge of the structure and properties of metals which makes it possible to predict with great accuracy the way a metallic object of known shape and composition will behave in any given environment. During the time that this corpus of knowledge was amassed, no single example of 'spoon bending' ever turned up; had it done so, then some of the foundations of metallurgy would have had to be revised. The scientist is therefore sceptical because he thinks it is very unlikely that metallurgy is based on shaky foundations; indeed the incredible success of all forms of metal technology indicates that the foundations are rock solid. Would people be so willing to fly in jet aeroplanes if they seriously believed that there were unknown forces at work which could bend or influence at a distance essential metal components? It is far more likely that Geller is simply a clever conjurer than that such forces actually exist.

Another example is also illuminating. Some years ago the Indian botanist C. J. Bose carried out a large number of experiments on plants which he claimed demonstrated the existence of rhythmic or pulsating structures analogous to the circulatory system of animals.[7] Other plant physiologists were sceptical because they had not been able to record the same rhythms using essentially the same simple equipment that Bose had. As more sensitive electronic equipment became available, numerous experiments were carried out which completely failed to confirm any of Bose's claims. Nevertheless in recent years there have been numerous claims by non-professionals that plants have complex sensory responses, that they feel pain, and even that they respond to language, music, and so on. (Of course, the non-professionals I refer to, often use equipment which seems on the face of it to be sophisticated enough to 'prove' the conclusions they are claiming. They may also resort to technical jargon to make their case sound more convincing.) A book on this subject has become a best seller[8] and this can only be possible because the readers who take it seriously are unaware of the enormous amount of research carried out by plant physiologists, which conclusively demonstrates the absence of a sensory system or any structures which would allow plants to respond to external stimuli in the way that animals do. The problem is again the difference in knowledge between the informed scientist and the uninformed layman, or more particularly, the failure to make the general public aware that the knowledge actually exists.

The point can also be illustrated by the story of the square egg. It is possible to buy a device which will compress a shelled hard-boiled egg into a cube, albeit with rounded edges. Demonstrating the egg, the statement can be made that chicken breeders have now produced a strain which lays square eggs. Non-scientists may accept this, holding the view that breeders can now produce all manner of weird varieties. Biologists who know something about the way eggs are formed in the hen's oviduct would certainly be more sceptical and at least ask to see the square egg with its shell, if not demand further evidence than that.

I referred at the beginning of this chapter to the philosophers who do not believe it is possible that the success of science can be attributed in such large part to the essentially illogical procedure of inductive reasoning. No review of scientific methodology would be complete without reference to the views of the most important and influential of these philosophers, namely Karl R. Popper. Popper has rejected the validity of the inductive method. Indeed he believes that the conventional view of the way science advances is totally incorrect, and that he has solved the problem of the illogical basis of induction.[9] He correctly points out that scientists never make observations at random: all their work is related to a particular theory or hypothesis. The crucial initiating event is therefore the formulation of a hypothesis which makes predictions that can be examined by experiment. A scientific hypothesis *necessarily* makes predictions; any that does not, is not part of science. Predictions can be confirmed by experiment or they can be refuted. Therefore *all* scientific hypotheses are, in principle, refutable or falsifiable. Confirmation of a prediction will strengthen a hypothesis, but it will not prove or establish it. Popper argues that the actual practice of science is to try to improve, modify, or refute hypotheses. This process inevitably leads to the acquisition of new knowledge, but never to complete certainty.

Much of what I have written in the earlier part of this

chapter is compatible with Popper's arguments, but I believe that working scientists are likely to come to the conclusion that he is discussing only one part of the whole corpus of scientific research. He tends to draw his examples from physics rather than biology. He also concentrates on the importance of the minority of scientists who, by imaginative insight, formulate new theories of hypotheses. Most working scientists, however, do not fall into this category. Their actual work is the collection of new information in the laboratory and it may have no obvious connection with any particular theory. Imagine a biochemist who has purified a large complex molecule, such as an enzyme (see Chapter 3). He wants to know more about it, so he examines in detail its chemical composition or its three-dimensional structure. This is not pedestrian observation, but involves highly sophisticated methods and a great deal of experience and skill. The result is that he may know more in the end about the way the molecule carries out its biological function and he will have provided more information about the structure of enzymes. None of these observations needs be necessarily related to any hypothesis or theory. There may well be of course a hypothesis about the way the enzyme actually functions, but in practice it is not necessarily the aim of this biochemist to set out to try to examine that theory or refute it. Scientists do of course agree that a hypothesis is only of value if it makes specific predictions which can be tested. Yet no one enjoys trying to demolish a theory, particularly his own; it is far more satisfying to try and provide positive evidence for it. However, Popper is here logically correct because the positive approach of looking for confirmation of a prediction and the negative one of trying to refute a prediction amount to the same thing. In practice all realistic predictions will be examined and the theory either survives and is strengthened, or it is modified, or it is eliminated. I believe, however, that Popper may be going too far in asserting that all scientific theories are in principle refutable. I cited previously the example of the genetic code. Theories of the code were proposed, experiments were carried out which distinguished between theories, and finally the correct answer was obtained. The genetic code had been cracked. It is not now possible to refute this conclusion by further experimental observations. Of several competing theories, one has now been established and it is no longer falsifiable. (It may, of course, be modified for some organisms which have not yet been studied.) Again, it is impossible not to accept the truth of Mendel's laws of inheritance, or the structure of innumerable biochemical compounds. These are examples of exact knowledge, which are not in principle refutable.

It could be argued that Popper's description of the scientific method cannot be applied to some very important branches of science. For example, the study of the origin of life could be said to be outside science, because any hypothesis will never be open to direct experimental investigation—at least on this planet. Nevertheless chemists have shown that very complex molecules can arise from simple ones, under appropriate laboratory conditions. It is quite likely in the future that replicating (i.e. dividing) molecules will be synthesized from inorganic components. It would be perverse to believe that these experiments tell us nothing about the origin of life on this planet, because that topic is outside scientific investigation.

For these reasons, I believe that Popper's description of scientific methodology is to some extent incomplete. Almost everything he says may be correct and illuminating, but there is more in science, perhaps especially in biological science, that he does not include in his overall thesis. The strength of a conclusion does indeed depend on the overall weight of evidence and, as I have explained, this in large part does involve multiple observation, or if you like, the principle of simple enumeration. As I pointed out at the beginning of this chapter, scientists are on the whole unaware, or uninterested, in the philosophy underlying their work. They can still be extremely successful in their research, but that is not to say that they would not be more successful if they did take note of the basic principles. In some fields the 'natural history' approach is very common, that is, the mere collection and publication of facts. Science is certainly more intellectually satisfying and enjoyable if a theoretical framework is proposed which can be tested by meaningful experiments. It is a pity therefore that some experimental scientists sneer at theoretical ones, simply because they are not doing hard work at the bench. In my view, there is a place for scientists who spend *all* their time sifting through the vast amount of experimental data which is continually accumulating in scientific journals and libraries. If they can reduce it to order and formulate new testable theories they are contributing to science as much, perhaps more, than is the skilled experimentalist.

As I have several times stressed, there is above all a need to break down the barriers of communication between scientists and non-scientists. To do this involves effort on both sides, but it also involves understanding the reasons why science is such a successful way of obtaining new and exact knowledge.

# 3. Molecular biology

The ultimate aim of the modern movement in biology is in fact to explain all biology in terms of physics and chemistry.

Francis Crick[1]

LIVING organisms can be examined by scientists at many different levels. Initially the shapes and external features were described and classified. Then anatomists studied the arrangement of internal structures and discovered that particular limbs or organs are made up of specific kinds of tissue such as muscle, nerves, blood, cartilage, and so on. The advance of microscopy resulted in the fundamental observation that all tissues are made up of cells. Tissues are entirely composed of particular kinds of cells (blood cells, epithelial cells, muscle cells, neurones, etc.) or material produced by cells, such as bone, serum, or keratin in skin and hair. Tissue-specific cells vary greatly in their shape and appearance under the microscope, but their basic structure and organization is very similar. Although there are exceptions, the size of cells in animals is also surprisingly constant. They are very small: a man of average size contains about $10^{13}$ of them (ten million million). If joined end to end, they would form a line less than one-fiftieth of a millimetre wide and about a hundred thousand kilometres long. Cells from plants have a similar organization to those in animals, but they have a rigid cell wall which normally prevents movement. On the other hand bacterial cells are quite different; they are much smaller and have quite a distinct microscopic structure, although as we shall see, their underlying chemical composition is essentially the same as animal and plant cells.

From the study of cells at the beginning of the century scientists started to examine and understand two fundamental features of living organisms; the sciences of biochemistry and genetics were born. Biochemists analysed the chemical composition of cells and together with physiologists they learned a great deal about the way cells function. It was shown that living organisms obey the basic laws of thermodynamics. That

23

is, the energy present in the food taken in can be exactly accounted for in the production of heat, movement, the synthesis of the components of cells which is necessary for growth, and a residue which is secreted or excreted. For the first time it was shown that organisms are in reality machines, with a complex chemical composition. No evidence was obtained which suggested that biological systems had special 'vitalistic' principles, which distinguished them from the inanimate world of chemistry and physics. It is also remarkable that living organisms are largely composed of very few of the chemical elements, namely carbon, oxygen, nitrogen, hydrogen, sulphur, and phosphorus. Some metals and a few other elements are present in lower amounts, and inorganic salts are an essential component of the aqueous environment inside and outside cells.

Biochemistry also showed that cells are in effect made up of many small organic molecules, or metabolites, and very large ones, such as proteins, with not so many of intermediate size. Small molecules might be sugars, which are broken down in respiration to form a series of derivatives, each simpler than the last, with the storage of energy in the form of another small molecule known as adenosine triphosphate or ATP. Other important small molecules are amino acids and it was surprising that there always seemed to be just twenty kinds of amino acid. According to the organism these are either taken in as food or synthesized, with consumption of energy, from simpler molecules. Amino acids in proteins are always in one of two possible isomeric forms (the *laevo* or L form), whereas those synthesized chemically in the laboratory consist of an equal mixture of L and D forms. (Isomers are defined by their molecular configuration which causes either *laevo* or *dextro* optical rotation of plane-polarized light.) Another two classes of small organic molecules are those known as the purines and the pyrimidines. There are two common types of purine (called adenine and guanine) and three types of pyrimidine (called uracil, thymine, and cytosine). Purines and pyrimidines are often attached to a sugar (ribose or deoxyribose) and one or more phosphates. In this form they are known as nucleotides. ATP is one such molecule. Somewhat larger than sugars, amino acids, purines, and pyrimidines are the lipids, which again are either found in the diet of the organism or are synthesized from simple components. Lipids were found to form part of the outer membrane of living cells, but they are also used in animals for storing energy in the form of fat.

The whole series of chemical reactions involving the synthesis and the break-down of these small organic molecules is known as *intermediary metabolism*. More than two thousand of these reactions have now been described in detail. Biochemists have also conclusively demonstrated that intermediary metabolism is essentially the same in animals, plants, and bacteria. Obviously, particular groups of organisms have special chemical abilities, such as photosynthesis in green plants, but by and large a fundamental biological principle has emerged: the basic components of living matter are the same in all organisms.

The large molecules in cells were far more difficult to study than the small ones. It was shown that a considerable proportion of the cell is made up of proteins, which consist of amino acids. It became clear that there are many different kinds of proteins and that many of them are essential for the reactions in intermediary metabolism. These are a collection of highly complex and efficient catalysts called enzymes, which make it possible for all the chemical transformations of small molecules to occur quickly and at the temperature of the organism. It was also clear that enzyme-mediated reactions obeyed the thermodynamic principles of chemistry. Enzymes did not provide or absorb energy, but often required high-energy compounds of low molecular weight, usually ATP, to carry out many of the reactions. In this period of biochemical research in the 1920s and 1930s, almost nothing was learned about the structure of protein molecules, although it was clear that they were the very stuff of life itself. Other large molecules were also identified, in particular ribonucleic acid (known as RNA) and deoxyribonucleic acid (known as DNA). Neither the detailed structure nor the function of these was known before the rise of molecular biology.

In parallel with all these biochemical studies, geneticists were vigorously following up the rediscovered experiments of Mendel. The most extensive series of experiments were carried out with the fruit fly *Drosophila melanogaster* by T. H. Morgan and his colleagues A. H. Sturtevant, C. B. Bridges, and H. J. Muller. In one of the most famous examples of sustained and collaborative research in science, most of the basic features of the mechanism of heredity were unravelled between about 1910 and 1920. It was shown that genetic factors called genes were discrete entities arranged in a linear array along visible structures called chromosomes. *Drosophila* has just eight small chromosomes, but other studies soon showed that the number, shape, and size of chromosomes varied enormously in different organisms. During the growth of cells the chromosomes are faithfully replicated, so that each cell in any one organism has the same number, with the exception of spermatozoa and unfertilized eggs, which have half this number. Chromosomes of animals and plants are contained within a membrane-bound vesicle in the cell called the nucleus, whereas the genetic material of bacteria is not membrane-bound. The part of the cell outside the nucleus, which is protein-rich, is called the cytoplasm. Genes were identified because they had particular effects on the appearance of the adult fly. They were shown to mutate—to change abruptly to a new form which had a different effect. For example, the normal fly has dark-red eyes, but many mutants were identified which had other eye colours. Mutations of genes were quite rare, but once they occurred they were stably inherited in their new form. It was also clear that the genes inherited from each parent were present as a maternal and a paternal set in every cell of an adult organism, but in the formation of the germ cells only one of the two copies of each kind of gene is included. As Mendel had first shown, there is an equal chance that any gene in a germ cell is of maternal or paternal origin. This means that the number of different kinds of germ cells from one adult can be extremely large and is easily sufficient to account for all the genetic variability which is seen in each plant or animal species. Many other features of the mechanism of transmission of genes from generation to generation were unravelled in *Drosophila* and other organisms but these cannot be reviewed here. It is important to emphasize, however, that the general properties and behaviour of genes and chromosomes turned out to be the same in all the species which were examined.

It became clear that there were very many genes on each chromosome and that they were self-reproducing structures too small to be examined by conventional microscopy. Geneticists speculated that genes might be large molecules with very specific properties, and the commonest view was that they might be proteins capable of producing exact copies of themselves. Geneticists did not in general think in biochemical terms, because their work depended largely on breeding experiments with quantitative analysis of the frequency of different types of progeny, with or without the use of microscopic techniques. There was one notable early exception to this: A. E. Garrod first realized that various inherited disorders were due to defects in intermediary metabolism.[2] He made the connection between changes or mutations in genes and a loss of the ability to carry out a single important chemical reaction. J. B. S. Haldane was also a pioneer in realizing the need to relate genetic and biochemical observations.

This then was roughly the situation up to the time of the Second World War. Biochemists and geneticists were not then in general communicating with each other and although W. T. Astbury had introduced biophysical methods (X-ray diffraction) to study large biological molecules, the significance of this approach was not widely appreciated. Several seminal events occurred in the 1940s which completely changed the situation. The nuclear physicist Erwin Schrödinger wrote a book called *What is life?*[3] in which he discussed the known properties of genes in physical terms. He made the crucial point that the physical laws governing the behaviour of large populations of small molecules were essentially statistical, whereas genes were discrete entities to which statistical laws could not possibly be applied. He speculated that there might be a new set of chemical and physical laws to be discovered which could account for the unique properties of genes. This book issued a challenge to physicists and many of them were stimulated by it to move into the field of biology. At about the same time the phenomenon of bacterial transformation was being studied by Oswald Avery and his colleagues. It had been known for some years that dead bacteria of one strain produced some material which could change the properties of another live strain of the same species. Avery discovered that the material was in fact DNA (deoxyribonucleic acid) and the implication was that DNA was responsible for the heritable characteristics, at least for these bacteria. Other crucial experiments were being carried out by

George Beadle and Edward Tatum. Following the ideas of Garrod and Haldane, they were able to show in the fungus *Neurospora* that particular mutants could be isolated which lacked the ability to carry out particular reactions in intermediary metabolism. The one-gene–one-enzyme hypothesis was born and the long-awaited collaboration between geneticists and biochemists had begun. In subsequent years the organism which was studied in the greatest detail was the simple bacterium *Escherichia coli*. Much more is now known about its genetics and its biochemical make-up, as well as many features of growth and cell division, than about any other species.

In parallel with advances in molecular genetics, rapid progress was made in the study of the structure of proteins, including enzymes. Fred Sanger devised a method for unravelling the chemical structure of a protein, starting first with insulin. It turned out that the basic feature was the polypeptide chain—a specific linear sequence of amino acids, of which there are just twenty different kinds. The polypeptide chains of individual proteins usually consist of more than one hundred, but less than five hundred amino acids. It was first shown in human globin (the protein part of haemoglobin) that a single gene mutation, which causes the inherited disease sickle-cell anaemia, produces a change in just one of the amino acids in this particular polypeptide chain. These and numerous subsequent studies proved that the properties of each protein were intrinsically determined by their sequence of amino acids. At the same time Linus Pauling, Max Perutz, and John Kendrew were determining the three-dimensional structure of proteins by the methods of X-ray diffraction. Proteins were not amorphous imprecise structures, but had a very specific shape. It became clear that the sequence of amino acids in a polypeptide chain strictly determined the way the chain folded up to form a precise three-dimensional structure. A mutation leading to a change in an amino acid could change the shape and thereby alter or destroy the function of the protein. Although proteins are complex molecules, they are very small in relation to the size of a single cell. Lined up side by side there would be about one thousand across the width of a single cell, and the total number of protein molecules in one animal cell might be in the range of ten to a hundred million.

Chemists had shown that DNA was a long linear polymeric molecule with a backbone consisting of alternating sugar (deoxyribose) and phosphate groups. To each sugar was attached one of the four bases, adenine, guanine, thymine, or cytosine. Maurice Wilkins and Rosalind Franklin studied the structure of DNA by X-ray diffraction and these and other observations led to the famous discovery by James Watson and Francis Crick of the DNA double helix in 1953.[4] This has rightly been regarded as one of the most important initiating events in the field of molecular biology. First, it had been established that the genetic material was in fact DNA. The genetic information in DNA could only be due to the linear sequence of the four bases, since nothing else in the structure varied. The alphabet of the genetic code must therefore have just four letters. Second, in the double-helix structure adenine was always paired with thymine and guanine was always paired with cytosine. This immediately suggested a mechanism for exact copying of genes. The separation of the strands provided two *templates* for the laying down of complementary DNA chains. The simple rule of base-pairing explained in principle how a DNA molecule could divide into two identical molecules. Third, the molecular basis of gene mutation must be an alteration in the sequence of bases; most simply, a substitution of one base pair for another base pair. Guido Pontecorvo, Seymour Benzer, and others had demonstrated by genetic methods that the gene was not an indivisible particle; it had a one-dimensional linear structure. Different mutations in a particular gene occurred at different points in this structure. This fitted in exactly with the idea that mutations are due to base changes in the linear structure of DNA. Chromosomes are also linear structures and they contain DNA. It is now known that the DNA of each chromosome is a continuous enormous molecule containing many genes in tandem array. The largest human chromosomes contain about five centimetres of DNA.

It now became apparent that the one-dimensional structure of DNA was directly related to the one-dimensional polypeptide structure of protein. An important advance was the demonstration that the linear order of individual mutations in a gene corresponded to the linear order of individual amino acid changes in the protein coded for by that gene. However the main problem was to explain how the four-letter DNA code defined or was translated into the sequence of the twenty kinds of amino acid. The solving of the genetic code depended on knowing the mechanism of protein synthesis. This turned out to be quite complex and it will be reviewed here only in the briefest outline. It had been realized early on that the assembly of polypeptide chains could not be due to the addition of amino acids, one by one, by specific enzymes. To synthesize each protein or enzyme would involve many, perhaps hundreds, of enzymes, and clearly this was on simple numerical grounds an impossibility. Instead, proteins must be synthesized on a template which defines the amino acid sequence. What happens is that DNA is first transcribed into an RNA message with the same sequence of bases (except that the base uracil always replaces thymine). The message is decoded on ribosomes, which are complex structures in the cytoplasm of cells, containing RNA and many different kinds of protein molecules. The decoding process involves small 'transfer' RNA molecules, one for each type of amino acid. Transfer RNA molecules attached to single amino acids and ribosomes ensure that in the assembly of the growing polypeptide chain, amino acids are added one by one in the correct order, as specified by the sequence of bases in the messenger RNA. A brilliant series of genetic and biochemical investigations, particularly by Francis Crick, Sydney Brenner, Marshall Nirenberg and Ghobind Khorana, and Severo Ochoa, led to the unravelling of the genetic code, which is undoubtedly the most impressive overall achievement of molecular biology. Three bases specify one amino acid. Since there are four types of base, sixty-four triplets exist and as only twenty amino acids are present in proteins, the code is therefore 'degenerate'. Individual amino acids are coded for by only one triplet or up to six triplets. Three triplets act as punctuation marks; they signal the termination of a polypeptide chain. One triplet signals the initiation of a chain, but it also codes for a particular amino acid, methionine. This is usually removed from the beginning of the chain by a specific enzyme.

Following his success with protein sequencing, Fred Sanger also developed methods for determining the sequence of bases in RNA and then in DNA. Recently he and his colleagues have determined the complete sequence of 5375 bases in the genetic material of a small bacterial virus. A single human chromosome, containing five centimetres of DNA, would have about 150 million bases. There are now many cases where it has been proved that the sequence of bases in DNA is exactly that expected from the sequence of amino acids in a protein. Indeed from just looking at the DNA base sequence one can deduce the structure of the protein it codes for. The use of Sanger's and other related methods will result in the future in the accumulation of a vast library of DNA sequences from a wide variety of living organisms. This will inevitably lead to a much more thorough understanding of gene structure and function.

One of the major problems in molecular genetics is to understand why genes sometimes actively produce proteins whereas at other times they are completely inactive or 'switched off'. It had been known for many years that a bacterial cell would synthesize an enzyme only if a correct substrate (i.e. the chemical on which the enzyme acts) was added to the medium. This mechanism of adaptation was finally elucidated by Francois Jacob and Jaques Monod. They deduced that a protein, called a repressor, bound to a specific site near the gene for the enzyme and prevented transcription, that is, the synthesis of messenger RNA. However, when the inducing substrate molecules entered the cell a few became attached to the repressor and altered its shape in such a way that it no longer bound to the DNA. The messenger RNA could now be synthesized, or *transcribed*, from DNA and this was then *translated* into the required enzyme. Many regulatory systems have now been worked out in bacteria or their viruses and the complete structure of repressor proteins is known. It is clear that specific interactions between proteins and DNA are of vital importance in the control of cellular functions.

In recent years, a family of enzymes has been discovered which cut DNA molecules at particular points: each enzyme is specific for a short sequence of bases, usually four or six. It is also possible to rejoin the DNA fragments, using other enzymes. This means that DNA molecules can be obtained where part of the molecule comes from one organism, usually the bacterium *Escherichia coli*, and the other part comes from another, such as man. DNA molecules of mixed origin can be grown in

*Escherichia coli* and their structure and properties can then be
studied in great detail. (This field is commonly known as
genetic engineering or genetic manipulation, but since these
terms are used in other contexts, I have suggested that it
should be referred to as *heterogenetics*.[5]) This powerful technique, in combination with others, has already led to many
recent spectacular advances in molecular biology, particularly our understanding of the detailed structure of genes in
higher organisms. There have been some surprises. For instance, genes of higher organisms often contain sequences of
DNA (intervening sequences or introns) which do not code for
any part of the polypeptide chain of the gene product. They
are removed at the RNA level, but their function is not yet
known.

Other branches of molecular and cell biology which have
been pursued with spectacular success are too numerous to
review. They include the synthesis and structure of antibody
molecules (proteins which inactivate substances foreign to the
body) and the properties of the cells called lymphocytes which
produce them; the properties of muscle proteins and the way
muscles contract; the structure of the basic chromosome thread
in higher organisms, which consists of DNA and repeating
units of groups of basic proteins called histones (nucleosomes);
the enzyme-mediated mechanisms which repair DNA damaged
by radiation or chemicals; the processes by which DNA is
actually replicated, by enzymes called DNA polymerases; the
study by electron microscopy of the detailed structure of
viruses, DNA molecules, and many subcellular components of
cells; the structure and function of mitochondria—a subcellular structure, or organelle, in the cytoplasm of cells which
carries out respiration; the structure and function of the cell
organelles of plants which contain chlorophyll, and the
mechanism of photosynthesis; the mechanism by which DNA
molecules are broken and rejoined (genetic recombination),
which leads to the reassortment of genes in the formation of
germ cells; the structure and morphogenesis of many viruses
and why they proliferate, or co-exist, within the cells they
invade.

The unrivalled success of molecular biology can be largely
attributed to the fact that different disciplines came together

in a concerted study of the basic units of living matter. Neither biochemistry, genetics, or biophysics alone could have achieved much progress, but in combination they provided an extremely powerful experimental methodology. However, success was by no means inevitable; it cannot be emphasized too strongly that it was completely dependent on the great intellectual ability, insight, and skill of many outstanding scientists. (It is remarkable that whereas the success of the theory of relativity made the name Albert Einstein a household word, the founders of molecular biology, several of whom I have mentioned, are scarcely known to the general public.) Another reason for the success is that the basic components of living matter turn out to be surprisingly simple. Who would have predicted thirty years ago that the genetic code would consist of just four different letters, that each word would have just three letters and that the code would be identical in all organisms? Of the very large number of possible amino acids only twenty are found in proteins. The underlying mechanism of genetic replication is simple to understand in principle, even if the details of the process turned out to be more complex than expected. It would not have been predicted that proteins are assembled on linear templates and that the primary sequence of amino acids itself determines the three-dimensional structure of the molecule and all its biochemical properties. No one could have guessed that the basic control circuits turning genes on and off could be so disarmingly simple. The assembly of quite complex structures, such as the bacterial viruses, turns out to require *only* the presence of many component proteins and DNA. The intrinsic properties of these proteins catalyse the morphogenesis of the complete virus and no complex assembly machinery is necessary. No doubt many subcellular structures are assembled in just the same way. Most important of all it turns out that complex macromolecules follow simple chemical laws. There is no need to invoke any new chemical or physical principle to explain the regular behaviour of genes or other cellular components. The nature of the various chemical bonds was discovered when the quantum theory of the atom was developed in the 1920s. There is nothing in molecular biology which is not explicable in quantum-mechanical terms.

A few years ago some scientists felt that most of the important problems had been solved and that molecular biology would tend to degenerate into a consolidating and academic discipline. This has turned out to be quite untrue. The speed of advance has been maintained and the range of biological problems to which molecular biology can be successfully applied seems to be unbounded. Nevertheless, there are enormous areas of ignorance in biology and some of these will be reviewed in later chapters. My prediction is that the power of the methods and techniques of modern biology will be easily sufficient to remove these areas of ignorance one by one, assuming of course that full support is provided for the necessary research.

# 4. Evolution by natural selection

A really beautiful mechanism, the discovery of which is
one of the great intellectual triumphs of our civilisation.

Once one has become adjusted to the idea that we are
here because we have evolved from simple chemical compounds by a process of natural selection, it is remarkable
how many of the problems of the modern world take on a
completely new light.

Francis Crick on natural selection[1]

LIVING organisms can be studied by scientists at various levels,
but they can only be *fully* understood in terms of their evolutionary origins. This is as true for man as for any other species.
Not only have all the biochemical, physiological, and genetic
processes necessary for the growth, maintenance, and reproduction of a human body been derived from a long process of
organic evolution, but also all those required for the function-
ing of the brain, language, and all the other unique features of
the behaviour of individuals or societies which distinguish the
human species from all other organisms. Charles Darwin,
together with Alfred Russell Wallace, provided the first comprehensive theory of evolution, which, in principle, was capable
of explaining both the extraordinary diversity of the form of
organisms and at the same time their common underlying
structural and chemical features. As we have seen all organisms
have essentially the same basic biochemical building blocks, the
same genetic material and genetic code, and use in their
proteins only one of the two possible isomeric forms of the
amino acids. It is therefore almost certain that life had a
common origin on this planet.

The extraordinary feature of the process of natural selection
is that it can create order where previously disorder existed,
and from one level of order it can subsequently create greater
and greater levels of complexity. The basic principles of
natural selection can be well illustrated by a brief outline of the
way life might have evolved in the first place even though the
details of this process are speculative. (Leslie Orgel has written
an excellent review of this field.)[2] Darwin was the first to realize

35

that before life existed organic compounds could accumulate indefinitely in oceans, lakes or elsewhere, since there were no organisms to feed on them. (Nowadays almost any natural organic metabolite would be rapidly degraded or assimilated by one or another living organism.) It is now well established from laboratory experiments that many organic compounds, such as amino acids, purines, or pyrimidines, can be formed from simpler compounds, such as carbon dioxide, formaldehyde, methane, and ammonia; all of which probably existed on the primitive earth. These experiments involve using electrical discharge, ultraviolet light, or inorganic catalysts, all of which were and still are present on our planet. The accumulation of assorted potential metabolites would continue unabated to give a 'primeval soup' in which condensation or polymerization reactions could start to occur. The concentration of a random collection of polymeric molecules (short polypeptide chains or primitive nucleic acids) would increase, since most of these compounds are chemically quite stable. The critical point would come when one or perhaps many of these polymeric molecules tended to catalyse the aggregation of smaller components to form similar polymers. The separation of the polymer aggregates would constitute the first primitive type of reproduction. From this time on, natural selection at the molecular level would begin. Initially, replication would almost certainly be extremely inaccurate and many of the products formed would not themselves be capable of replication. Any molecule which reproduced itself with greater accuracy would tend to increase in numbers. The rate of increase would depend on the time it took to replicate, the efficiency or accuracy of replication and the availability of the smaller organic components in the primeval soup. Replicating molecules would now be competing with each other. It is easy to see that those with the most rapid rate of increase would outgrow the others. In evolutionary terminology they would be *selected for* and the others would be *selected against*. Although an increase in accuracy of replication would initially be a key factor, it is very likely that errors or mistakes would still be common. Thus whilst growing these replicating molecules would continually be generating new variant forms. A minor fraction of these would replicate a little faster than the parent, so they would tend to be selected and overtake the original population. Random chemical changes, or mutations, as we now call them, will through natural selection create more efficient replicating molecules.

The reader at this point might believe that the argument is based merely on fanciful speculation, since we can never have direct knowledge of the molecular events which occurred during the evolution of primitive macromolecules. In fact, ingenious experiments have now been done which clearly demonstrate that replicating molecules in test tubes are subject to natural selection.[3] All that is required is an RNA polymer, one enzyme capable of replicating it, and the four small basic nucleotide components of RNA.[2] The molecules replicate and have to be continually diluted by subculture to fresh test tubes with enzyme and substrates. It was found that after a time the rate of growth of the RNA speeded up—altered molecules were selected. Some of these were simply shorter. These 'little monsters' completed their replication faster than the original molecules; but more subtle changes could also be selected, for instance, the ability to grow in the presence of a compound which was initially inhibitory. These mutations were shown to be due to single changes in the sequence of RNA bases.

Returning now to the origin of life, a critical stage would be reached when the small components of the primeval soup began to be used up by the competing macromolecules. Now it would be an advantage to accumulate or concentrate in some way these small compounds, or metabolites, as we now call them, so that they were available for the replication process. There would be strong selection pressure for any polymer which was enclosed in its own small container or vesicle, filled with its own private supply of primeval soup. Membranous structures enclosing metabolites and replicating polymers could perhaps be described as the first organisms. Membranes might be made up mainly of sheets of polypeptides (called $\beta$ sheets), whereas replicating molecules would be nucleic acids, although not necessarily identical to those in present-day organisms. Clearly it would be advantageous if the nucleic acids could in some way direct the assembly of the polypeptides and thus the means to assemble the first primitive catalysts or enzymes would have to evolve. At a later stage the ability to synthesize metabolites would be strongly selected, since the supply available to these primitive cells would be continually dwindling.

None of these further details or refinements need concern us; the purpose of this brief review of the possible origin of organisms was simply to illustrate the ingredients of the process of evolution by natural selection. The basic principles are as follows. First, biological replication is necessary. Second, biological replication is logarithmic or exponential and therefore cannot be unlimited since resources are not infinite ($2^n$ is the number of descendants, where $n$ is the number of simple binary fissions; for $n = 50$ there are $10^{15}$, or a thousand million million descendants). Therefore descendants are necessarily competing against each other for survival. Third, during division new genetic variants appear. Many of these may multiply more slowly and are eliminated; any that grow faster will be more successful in the competition for living space and will be selected. Fourth, this overall process inevitably increases the efficiency of the replicating system and this involves increasing its complexity. Thus random genetic variation plus selection generates more and more order in biological systems, where previously there was total or relative disorder. It is clear that these conclusions run counter to the commonly held intuitive view that order and complexity can only be the result of purpose and design. Again and again, Darwinian natural selection has been opposed simply on the grounds that it is inconceivable that blind chance (i.e. mutation) could provide the basis for the evolution of all the highly complicated structures seen in advanced organisms. One of the difficulties many people have in grasping the power of natural selection seems to be a numerical one. In a sense it can be said that natural selection is simply a device for generating changes which have a high degree of improbability. It is indeed very improbable that an organism with such a fantastically elaborate structure as, for example, a lobster, could just be the result of random changes in the sequence of bases in DNA. But natural selection can change the low probability of each beneficial or improving mutation (perhaps one in a million individuals) into a one hundred per cent probability when that mutation replaces all other versions of the gene in question. If we need a thousand such mutations to generate a lobster from a simpler animal precursor, then natural selection has accomplished the task by systematically eliminating all the less advantageous mutations. The biological cost is enormous, but then so is the time scale in terms of the vast number of successive generations which have occurred before the contemporary version of the animal appears. Of course, mutations are not necessarily selected sequentially, those affecting quite different structures of the organism can be increasing concomitantly in the overall population.

The strength of the theory of natural selection is that it is the great unifying principle in biology. At the beginning of this century there was an unnecessary conflict between the Darwinian evolutionists and the geneticists who had rediscovered Mendel's laws. However, in the late 1920s three scientists, R. A. Fisher, J. B. S. Haldane, and Sewall Wright, made it clear that the theory of natural selection was totally compatible with the principles of Mendelian genetics. A much stronger theory therefore emerged and the important field of population genetics came into its own. Many population geneticists have been totally theoretical in their work, but others have studied plants and animals in their natural environments and have demonstrated beyond doubt the actual occurrence of Darwinian selection of genetic traits.

So far, I have not used the words *fitness* and *adaptation*, both of which are central in evolutionary theory. Darwinian fitness refers only to the ability of an organism to produce viable offspring (which themselves reach reproductive maturity) in relation to other members of the same species. A mutation can increase fitness and be selected, or reduce it and be eliminated. (It is incorrect to say that one species is fitter than another, for instance a lion cannot be said to be fitter than a mouse because of its size and strength, nor is the mouse fitter because of its reproductive capacity.) The process of evolution by natural selection inevitably leads to the adaptation of organisms to different environments. One way an organism can compete with others is to move into a new environment which was previously unoccupied. Thus we continually see the appearance of innovative structures which allow colonization of almost all possible environments. We say that a species is *adapted* to a particular ecological niche. What has frequently happened in evolution is that the initial adaptation of a completely new form capable of surviving in a new environment is a slow process, accomplished perhaps by only one or a very few species. But once the breakthrough has occurred and the colonization has begun, then a period of adaptive radiation occurs, leading to an endless proliferation of species, all of which are variations on a basic morphological scheme. This happened dramatically with the insects and also, of course, with the vertebrates. The evolution of an organism with an internal skeleton was followed by the appearance of fish, reptiles, birds, and mammals, and within each group there is incredible diversity upon the basic anatomical scheme of a skull, backbone, and two pairs of appendages or limbs. In evolutionary terms, it was easier for a whale to adapt limbs to form flippers, than it is to evolve flippers *de novo* and allow limbs to become vestiges. It is very hard for it to evolve a new respiratory system allowing it to breathe under water. Everywhere we see extraordinary diversity in the animal and plant kingdoms, but almost all of it is due to variation on basic taxonomic prototypes. Evolution by natural selection has certainly left many avenues unexplored, for instance, it has never produced large structures generating locomotion by rotation, such as wheels or propellers.

Selection acts on individual organisms, yet it is populations of individuals which evolve into new species. The interchange of genetic material within a species is normally brought about by sexual reproduction. This process makes it possible for a beneficial mutation in one individual to be combined with a different beneficial mutation in another. The offspring may be fitter than both parents. There is in a population a pool of genes which are continually being reassorted or recombined in new individuals. Selection acts on those individuals with the best combinations of genes and particular mutations become more or less frequent. (This is not to say that the origin and maintenance of the sexual process itself is easily understood; Maynard Smith has recently discussed the basic problems in his book *The evolution of sex*.[4]) It is increasingly clear that evolution does not act at the group or population level, and enormous confusion has arisen from loose discussion about the selection of genes which are for the benefit of the species as a whole, rather than for individuals which possess such genes. Normally genes can only spread in populations if they benefit individuals. The gene is propagated because it confers advantage on the organism which has the means to transmit it to offspring. At first sight it would seem that some genes would not be selected because they confer a disadvantage on the individual. For instance, genes for altruistic behaviour would seem to benefit other individuals and therefore should be selected against. In recent years many ingenious theoretical studies have provided convincing explanations for the origin of certain kinds of animal behaviour, which appear not to favour the individual displaying that behaviour. These depend in one way or another on the concept of kin selection or 'inclusive fitness': a gene with a deleterious effect on an individual can be selected if it favours the survival of closely related individuals which may also have the same gene. These advances in evolutionary theory have been admirably explained in non-mathematical terms by Richard Dawkins in his book *The selfish gene*.[5]

The process of evolution is ultimately based on the preservation and propagation of the genetic material, the DNA. The genes are concerned only with their own survival and will, in effect, explore all strategies to accomplish this end. Many fish produce billions of eggs and sperm to ensure that at least a few of the innumerable fertilized eggs survive to adulthood in the absence of any parental care. At the other extreme female mammals produce few eggs, nourish the embryo within the body of the female and take care of the offspring. Yet within the mammals, small rodents develop to adulthood very rapidly and reproduce very rapidly (mice produce about fifty offspring a year), whereas other species grow and reproduce very slowly (female elephants produce on average about four offspring in a lifetime). The strategy of the mouse is related to the fact that few offspring survive to breed, whereas the chance of a newborn elephant surviving to adulthood is enormously higher. The mouse and the elephant are merely very different types of biological machine, evolved to perpetuate their own DNA. In each species a distinct tactic or strategy has evolved to ensure the continuing transmission of its genes. Dawkins has pointed out that all organisms are 'survival machines' coded for by DNA to ensure its own perpetuation.

The basic biochemical and genetic system of man is in no way distinct from that of other organisms. In the evolution of primitive populations there could have been no specific point in time where it could have been said that man had finally appeared on earth. For a very long period the hunter–gatherer life-style of evolving man possibly did not strongly distinguish him from other primates, nor is there any reason to believe that he was initially more successful in reproductive ability and in increasing population size. All this is to state the obvious, but unfortunately the view that man appeared, by creation or otherwise, at a given point in time as a unique species, distinct from all others, is a far more widely held view. The vital phase in the evolution of man was clearly the adaptation which led to an ability to memorize large amounts of information and also the means to communicate this information from one individual to another. As Jaques Monod has convincingly argued, the crucial breakthrough must have been the ability to store knowledge in a community rather than an individual. This would have been of such enormous value to individuals within the community that there would be great selection pressure to increase this particular feature of the human brain.[6] Brain size in fact did evolve in primitive man at a rate very much faster than change in morphological or anatomical features of other mammals. This was almost certainly associated with the development of language and memory. It is important to realize that this is also part of an evolutionary strategy to transmit human genes. E. O. Wilson has made the point clearly:

The essence of the argument, then, is that the brain exists because it promotes the survival and multiplication of the genes that direct its assembly. The human mind is a device for survival and reproduction and reason is just one of its various techniques.[7]

From this point on social evolution became much more important than Darwinian evolution, because it was immeasurably more rapid. Instead of only genes being transmitted from generation to generation, all types of information gained by experience were also transmitted to give the corpus of knowledge we call culture. In a society with a cultural tradition, each new individual gained a head start in evading predators, in competing with other species for limited food resources and so on. This inevitably led to the colonization of more and more environments and to the increase in numbers of individuals, which makes man the dominant species today.

It has also inevitably led to the belief in almost all human societies that man has special properties, especially spiritual and moral qualities, which sharply distinguish him from all other species. It is said that only man has free will, a non-material soul, the ability to distinguish good from evil, and so on. What do concepts such as these actually amount to in biological terms? An enormous amount of information is now available about the biochemical composition and metabolism of human cells and tissues. It is in no way different from that of any other species. Of course, a particular human protein such as haemoglobin may have an amino acid sequence very slightly different from all other mammals, but then most species also have small differences from others. The genetic code and the mechanism of the inheritance of genes and chromosomes is the same in man as in other species. None of this is surprising, since man evolved from precursor species. With regard to his under-lying chemical composition there is simply no evidence what-soever that any particular novel features exist. Nor is it possible to envisage any particular point in time when a collection of animals, with genetic variability in intelligence, self-awareness, and so on, could be said to have broken through from a totally material basis to a condition which was more than that, namely, the acquisition of some of the non-material or extra-material features I have just mentioned. Then there is also the fact of the development of a human being from a single cell. At what point in time or organization of the developing body could it be reasonably said that these features actually arise? Discussion of such hypothetical topics seems to be as un-productive as medieval religious philosophers arguing about the size of angels, or whether Adam actually had a navel. Numerous attempts have been made by various authors to invoke the need for special vitalistic or non-material forces in man, or even in less advanced species. For instance, it has been claimed that DNA simply does not contain enough bits of information to code for a highly complex organism. The falsity of such arguments has been easily exposed by Francis Crick in his book *Molecules and men*.[1] Not only is there a complete absence of evidence for vitalistic principles, but there is no compelling reason to invoke them. The 'anti-reductionists' can claim that an organism is more than the sum of its component parts, but this view—as I mentioned in the Introduction—ultimately reduces to a disagreement between them and molecular biologists about the definitions of terms. What does 'more than the sum of its component parts' actually mean?

Consider, for example, the question of free will which has been discussed by philosophers over the centuries. When someone is asked to move either his right or his left arm, he is apparently free to choose between the possibilities and an observer could never predict which it would be. The subject is said to be exercising his free will. The impulse to move, say, his right arm, comes from the brain. It originates as an electrical and chemical signal from one or a group of neurones. The sudden activity of these cells does not arise *de novo*, in other words, energy is not spontaneously created where none previously existed; clearly the signal must be the result of some other prior stimulation or impulse. Part of that stimulation is the request to move an arm, but part is a selection or choice mechanism in the subconscious mind. Similarly, computers can be 'asked' to generate events (e.g. flashing a red or a green light) at random and there is no way to predict their 'choice', but no one would say they had free will. People undoubtedly have the sensation of free will, but only because they are aware of the last link of a causal chain. If there really *was* free will, it would be a miracle—a contradiction of the law of conservation of energy!

Some vitalists who are aware of the above argument have even gone so far as to invoke Heisenberg's uncertainty principle to provide a basis for free will. Because it is not possible to predict the position of electrons in an atom, they extrapolate to elements of unpredictability in brain or neurone function. This must be a completely unjustified red herring, since the uncertainty principle has no direct relevance to the way chemical reactions actually occur in the living cell. As molecular biology has proved, the manner in which simple or complex biological molecules behave in cells is extremely predictable. The only random elements in biological systems are various kinds of errors, for example when a wrong amino acid is inserted into a protein or a wrong base into DNA to produce a mutation. These errors may be of great significance for the organism (for example in the process of ageing[8]), but they cannot be of significance in the working of the human mind.

Man is also thought to be unique in having a conscience and the ability to distinguish good from evil. However, social anthropologists have certainly amassed enough information to demonstrate conclusively that behaviour which is regarded as good in one society may be evil in another. Our conscience and moral code is the product of our evolutionary origins and the cultural evolution which has been superimposed on this. Cultural evolution has been different in different societies; so the moral code is also different.

Man has evolved to a particular state of consciousness, or self-awareness, although it is far from clear whether or not higher animals can be said to experience consciousness. The unique feature of man is his knowledge, memory, or experience of the past and his expectation of the future. For example, he knows he will die in a way that an animal does not. However, an isolated individual would not have this particular aspect of self-awareness: knowledge of death is the result of communication with parents or others during childhood. Reference is often made to the 'problem of consciousness', but it is not clear to me why this should imply that there are non-material components in our brain. The basic problem is that we are totally ignorant of the structure and function of the human brain, including, of course, the neurological basis for the difference between the conscious and subconscious. But to be ignorant provides no justification for a belief in a uniquely human non-molecular soul or spirit which has somehow 'emerged' from lower forms, or has in some way been implanted. It is far more realistic to believe that the special properties of the human brain, including consciousness, have a physical basis and that they evolved from a lower level of complexity by natural selection. I shall argue later that the structure and function of the human brain is amenable to scientific investigation and that it will ultimately be understood in cellular and molecular terms.

Darwin's *Origin of species* provoked bitter controversy because religious people correctly understood that it was a threat to their established views. The controversy has largely died down, partly because the overwhelming significance of the theory of natural selection has been swept under the carpet. When it is taught in schools and universities, it is usually given cursory treatment, and the fact that it is relevant to every aspect of human life is rarely made clear. The controversy has also greatly declined because many religious people appear to have assimilated the concept of evolution into their beliefs and doctrines. In point of fact they have not done so, because they still maintain as a central feature of their doctrine that man has a non-material soul or spirit which guides his behaviour and may survive after his death. The argument that this could evolve by the natural selection of random mutations cannot be sustained with any seriousness and, indeed, it is not accepted by most religious people. Therefore, they are still rejecting Darwinian evolution as far as man himself is concerned.

In recent years there has been a renaissance of interest in the theory of evolution. This stems from the connections which have been made between population genetics, ecology and animal behaviour. In particular the interest in the evolution of various forms of behaviour, has given rise to the new science of sociobiology.[9] Since some of the arguments and conclusions can be applied to man himself, it is not surprising that sociobiology has already given rise to considerable controversy. Criticism so far, however, has come mainly from scientists with left-wing opinions rather than from religious groups. I will return to the subject of sociobiology in a later chapter.

In concluding this one, I shall predict that the new important advances in our understanding of evolution by natural selection, coupled with our ever-increasing knowledge of the physical and chemical basis of all life, including man, will inevitably generate a new controversy between science and religion which may dwarf that which followed the publication of the *Origin of species*. It could lead to the demise of religions or their retreat to a position which can be no more than a belief in certain ethical codes. Alternatively, in view of the strength and ubiquity of religious feeling in many parts of the world, there could be attempts to suppress the practice of science itself. In my view, scientists should be made aware of this danger.

# 5. Science unlimited

I do not believe that there is any intrinsic limitation upon
our ability to answer the questions that belong to the
domain of natural knowledge and fall therefore within the
agenda of scientific enquiry.

P. B. Medawar[1]

In a previous chapter I reviewed the extraordinary success of
molecular biology in revealing the basic chemical features of
living organisms. What I did not do was to explain that many
areas of biology are not understood at all. It is particularly
difficult for non-scientists to know, even in very general and
vague terms, the boundary between exact knowledge and lack
of knowledge in science. Even scientists themselves, happily
plodding along in a well-established field of research which is
readily amenable to experimental investigation, often seem to
be unaware of some of the fundamental unanswered questions
which will stimulate more original and exciting research in the
future.

We saw that in the history of biology, study started at the
macroscopic level and progressively moved down to the microscopic and finally to the molecular level. The future task of
biology is now to proceed in the reverse direction, so that each
layer of new understanding is based on a solid foundation of
certain knowledge of the lower or preceding layer. Before
enlarging on this theme, let me first enumerate some of the
basic features of living cells about which we are still ignorant.
More is known about the simple bacterium *Escherichia coli* than
any other organism, but how it assembles its various macromolecules in the precisely organized way which is necessary for
cell division is not known. There is of course much information
about this process, but the complete synthesis, the complete
description, is not yet available. We have even less knowledge
about animal and plant cells. The way chromosomes divide
during cell division (*mitosis*) has been studied for a very long
time and the principles underlying the process can be said to
be understood: but all the molecular details are certainly not

47

known. With regard to the actual mechanism of overall division of cells with defined nuclei, then we are in a state of almost complete ignorance. We are also largely unaware of the forces which govern the shapes and sizes of cells, even bacterial cells. Of course, it is clear why a neurone has many long extensions called axons; they are necessary for making connections (or synapses) with other neurones; but we have no idea how these cells actually develop and maintain the form they do. Cells are bounded by membranes and it is now increasingly clear that membranes often have a far more complex function than just enclosing the cytoplasm. For example, membranes control what goes in and what comes out of cells. Also, cells in higher organisms undoubtedly transmit chemical signals to each other and membranes play a central role in this process. Nevertheless, the detailed structure of no single cellular membrane has yet been unravelled.

Very complete anatomical descriptions of the development of embryos have been available since the end of the last century, but the reason a particular fertilized egg develops in just the way it does is almost totally obscure. In the development of organisms, there is both a temporal unfolding of a particular programme and also a means of organizing cells in three-dimensional space. The molecular mechanisms involved are at the moment largely a matter for speculation. It is not even known how particular genes are switched on or off at specific times during development, although, as we have seen, this has been fully explained in the case of the regulation of bacterial genes. With regard to tissue function, there is often very precise information, but also complete ignorance. The physiology of the nerve impulse along an axon is well understood and much is known about the mechanism whereby impulses are trans-mitted from cell to cell; yet the nature of the specificity of the cell connections, which must be the fundamental feature of even the most primitive nervous system, is still a complete mystery. Again, the molecular mechanism by which muscle contracts is largely understood, but we do not know how cells differentiate and organize themselves to form muscle tissue and, even more important, how the very specific pattern of inner-vation, which allows them to be controlled by the central nervous system, is set up.

Scientists have often been far too optimistic in believing they can find easy answers to some of the crucial questions that can be asked about cell and tissue function. It seems all too obvious that if a scientist is interested, for instance, in such a fundamental problem as the development of an embryo from a fertilized egg, then he should choose a suitable species (such as an amphibian or sea urchin) where the behaviour and organization of cells can be conveniently studied. I choose this example because it provides a clear illustration of the way in which research in a particular field can stagnate. In the last years of the nineteenth century and the early years of this century, the anatomy of embryos at various developmental stages was carefully observed and described. However, no progress was made towards an understanding of the *mechanism* of development. The famous embryologist H. Dreisch became so pessimistic about finding a solution, that he invented the vitalistic principle, the entelechy, which he thought somehow directed the overall process of development.[2] The need to suggest something as nebulous as the entelechy is a proof of failure in research. For decades after the work of Dreisch and his contemporaries, little significant progress was made in this field. Only in recent years have new ideas been forthcoming about some of the forces which may determine an embryo's development, and, more important, techniques of molecular biology have been applied, particularly by John Gurdon and his collaborators, to answer very important questions about the proteins and nucleic acids of the unfertilized eggs of amphibians. Also, new techniques involving the manipulation of single cells or groups of cells which are marked by particular gene mutations, are revealing much new information about early mammalian development.

It is highly significant that success in a complex field of research is often achieved when a combination of scientific disciplines is focused on a common problem. The science of immunology is a case in point. There has been an explosion of information in the last fifteen years or so, and this has come from the development of new qualitative and quantitative techniques for detecting and measuring antigens (substances foreign to the organism) and antibodies (proteins which destroy or inactivate antigens or foreign cells); the unravelling of the chemical structure of the polypeptide chains of antibodies;

the characterization of the different types of lymphoid and other cells which make up the immune system, and the use of classical Mendelian genetics, as well as the more modern techniques of somatic-cell genetics, in which different types of lymphoid cells are fused and their hybrids analysed. Thus the combination of biochemistry, cell biology, and genetics has suddenly catalysed rapid progress in the field of research which was pioneered by Paul Erhlich, Elie Metchnickoff, and others seventy years ago, but which made rather slow progress for fifty years thereafter. Another example of rapid acceleration in research is in the study of viruses which infect animal cells. Again the ingredients have been the same: detailed information about the chemical organization of the DNA (and in some cases RNA) of the virus particle and its proteins; the molecular architecture and three-dimensional structure which is revealed by electron microscopy; the isolation of gene mutations which affect essential viral processes, and the use of these and other methods to study the way cells and viruses actually interact with each other. In a word, the techniques of molecular biology have transformed the animal virologist's world.

We can now return to the many unsolved problems and ask how and when solutions to these can be expected. As I have indicated, we can expect that the acquisition of complete knowledge at the cellular, tissue, and macroscopic levels will utterly depend on an understanding of the molecular components involved. I have already suggested that biology will, in general, have to proceed in the reverse direction from that which gave rise to molecular biology itself. It would be stupid to try to predict an exact order of discoveries, but it is not hard to anticipate the general sequence of advances which may be expected. A complete understanding of cell division in simple organisms such as bacteria will soon be available. Indeed the knowledge of *Escherichia coli* will eventually reach a point where all the chemical components are known and their interactions fully understood. At that time it would in principle be possible to synthesize all these components and to assemble them to form a living bacterial cell. As Francis Crick has pointed out, such an exercise would be very costly and not particularly worth while.[3] (It would, however, presumably convince the few remaining vitalists who believe that even a bacterial cell is more than the sum of its chemical components.) At some later time a similar molecular understanding of cells with nuclei will be achieved, first simple ones like yeast, and then mammalian cells grown in culture. Long before that, the mechanism which switches genes on or off during development will become understood. This will open up a huge new field of research in which the essential differences in gene expression between cells of different tissues will be discovered. In consequence the chemical basis of cell specialization, or differentiation, will be revealed.

As I have mentioned, the two central unanswered problems in development are the means by which the genetic programme is unfolded in the correct temporal order and the way in which cells and tissues organize themselves in three-dimensional space to form the whole organism. The first will primarily involve the analysis of the sequence of changes in gene activity and the characterization of the various regulatory or controlling gene products. The second will depend on the identification of the specific surface proteins of cells which allows them to recognize or distinguish between other cells, and also the chemical nature of the signalling which occurs between cells which are not in contact. Much is already known about the biochemical signalling by hormones, which usually act over larger distances (for instance, by circulating in the blood-stream). It is at present believed that short-range signalling in cell aggregates is also very important in the morphogenesis of tissues, limbs, and so on, but our understanding of the nature of these signals so far is obscure. The identification of signalling devices is by itself insufficient to explain cell behaviour: it is also essential to identify the specific molecular effects they have on gene activity.

I emphasized previously that progress in molecular biology was entirely due to the skill, insight, and hard work of ex-ceptionally talented scientists in several fields. We should not underestimate the difficulties ahead in unravelling the prob-lems I have just outlined. Advances will be completely depen-dent upon experimental work of the highest quality, combined with those particular intellectual abilities which make it possible to construct at each stage a rock-solid theoretical framework on which further advances can be based.

In solving the problems of the development of multicellular organisms, it is likely that many different species will be used, but it is not likely that the first major breakthroughs will be made with advanced species, such as mammals. The main reason for this is the one I have just mentioned, namely, that an essential component of the research will be genetics, particularly the use of mutants with specific alterations in gene expression or in developmental processes. Among mammals, the house or laboratory mouse *Mus musculus* has been the most extensively studied genetically, but it is hard to see how this work could be extended to achieve the degree of sophistication which is now seen in bacteria, viruses, yeasts, or the fruit fly *Drosophila*. Molecular biologists have already anticipated this problem and several have initiated long-term studies of simple multicellular organisms. For example, Sydney Brenner and his colleagues have in the last few years developed the genetics of a small roundworm or nematode, which can be handled very easily under laboratory conditions. At the same time they have used electron microscopy to describe in great detail the cellular organization of the organism, and other studies have charted the development of the nervous system of the animal. Many mutants affecting, for example, muscle or nervous function are now available for further experiments. Another possible organism is the famous fruit fly *Drosophila*, on which so much of the science of genetics was based. It turns out that this organism is also appropriate for many biochemical studies and for analysis of the function of the nervous system. Seymour Benzer has isolated a series of intriguing mutants which have fundamental effects on the animal's behaviour. Some are unable to learn, like the mutant *dunce*; others fail to respond to external stimuli, or are paralysed when the temperature is raised, because they have a protein which is essential for the transmission of nerve impulses, that has been altered to become temperature sensitive. It is interesting that classical neurophysiologists would not dream of choosing a tiny organism like *Drosophila* for their experiments; it was in fact a molecular geneticist, Obaid Siddiqi, who first showed that it was quite feasible to insert microelectrodes into single *Drosophila* neurones and record their activity.

Important advances frequently depend on the choice of

experimental material. A classic instance of this was the brilliant realization by Max Delbruck that if genetics was to be understood at the molecular level, then very simple organisms have to be used. He pioneered such studies with a virus of *Escherichia coli* known as bacteriophage T4. I suspect that breakthroughs in the study of developmental processes will also depend on choosing the correct organism. Whichever ones are used, there is little doubt that progress will depend on the same combination of scientific disciplines which catalysed advances in molecular biology.

Although such a combined approach is often not yet possible with very complex organisms, let me make it clear at this point that I am not implying that the use of these organisms in biological research is premature or a waste of time. The situation is that important information can be gained using one experimental approach, but it is unlikely that a complete answer to any given problem will be obtained. The information will fall into place at some later point in time, when other approaches have filled in the gaps in knowledge. Let me give a specific example. Classical and modern experimental neurophysiology has provided much information about the organization and function of the central nervous system of higher organisms, such as mammals or amphibia. Is it possible, however, to believe that the methods which have so far been used will explain in principle how the brain of one of these organisms actually functions? Since the specificity of neural connections must in one way or another depend on macromolecules, I cannot see how brain function can be understood in detail without knowing what at least some of these molecules actually are. Now, that is not to say that all neurobiologists should plunge into molecular studies; many of them maintain that such studies would be premature. They believe it is first essential to uncover the general principles governing specificity of neural connections, before searching for molecules. This view may be correct, but nevertheless it will ultimately be necessary to undertake genetic and molecular studies, and I suspect that this will first be done with much simpler animals. Only at some later time will the information already obtained with more complex systems become understood at a molecular level.

In a progressive understanding of the development, function

and organization of higher organisms, it is obvious that the nervous system poses special problems. The reason is that the cells making up this part of the organism not only have the biochemical specificity expected of any other specialized tissue, but have, in addition, the means of transmitting electrical signals along exactly defined cellular pathways. Thus an additional layer of specificity is imposed on neurones which is not present in other cells and this is essential for the exact cell–cell interactions which build up the circuits and networks of the central nervous system.

We can therefore be fairly sure that the way nerve cells organize themselves will be understood only after it has been discovered how almost all other types of cells and tissues carry out their functions. Moreover, beyond the complexity of neural connections there lies the further problem of memory and complex behaviour. There can be little doubt that in any species of mammal, the brain is by far the most complex component of the body and it will therefore be the last to be fully understood in molecular and cellular terms. In mammals, other than man, there are not enormous differences in brain function, although there are large differences in brain size. It is not very likely that a small mammal, such as a lemur, has a brain with a less sophisticated function than say, that of an elephant, which has an enormously larger brain. It is therefore likely that the full understanding of the brain of one mammal, such as a mouse, will tell us most of what we want to know about other mammals. It will, of course, tell us a great deal about the human brain as well.

As I mentioned in a previous chapter, the evolution and success of man was undoubtedly associated with the development of the means to store information in his memory and the ability to communicate by language. Therefore on top of all the complexity seen in the brain of any other mammal there is clearly another layer of complexity in the human brain. We can draw the obvious conclusion that the human brain is the most complex biological object that exists on this planet and therefore represents the ultimate challenge for biologists who wish to find out how it works. In addition to that, there is the additional problem that man is not an experimental organism. For these and other reasons it is widely believed that an understanding of the human brain is beyond the reach of scientific research. In the rest of this chapter I shall argue against this view.

First, there is the general proposition that progress in science appears to be without limit. Again and again, prophecies have been made that such limits exist and these have been shown to be incorrect. A famous one was the widely held view that the chemicals found in organisms were somehow distinct from inorganic ones in the laboratory and that the former could never be synthesized from the latter. This was conclusively disproved more than a hundred years ago. Many biochemists believed for some years that proteins did not have a chemically defined structure which was amenable to experimental investigation. Fred Sanger proved they were wrong. There is not much doubt that anyone who predicted in 1952 (the year before the structure of DNA was unravelled) that the genetic code would be cracked within 15 years would have been laughed at by most geneticists or biochemists. Similarly, the sequencing of the bases in large tracts of DNA seemed an insuperable problem only a few years ago. Today advance is occurring at the same, if not an increasing rate and more and more fields are being penetrated by scientists employing the techniques of molecular biology.

Second, nature provides the experimental scientist with a wide range of organisms which is representative of the general path of evolutionary advance. In the case of nervous systems, every level of complexity can be found among existing species. It is impossible to believe that the simplest ones cannot be worked out in full detail by appropriate experimental investigation. From there on it is hard to see why each success should not be followed by an understanding of the next most complex system. During this time the general principles governing the development of neural connections and circuits will emerge and in all probability the mechanism for the storing of information in memory will be discovered. The eventual elucidation of brain function in animals such as insects, amphibia or mammals cannot fail to tell us a great deal about the human brain. Indeed, it may tell us most of the important things we need to know.

Third, man *is* available for scientific investigation even

without the possibility of the types of experiment which can be carried out on animals. Many methods of experimental psychology are applicable to man and these have revealed considerable information about, for example, sensory perception and certain aspects of behaviour. I do not think that such methods by themselves will yield too much information about brain function, but in conjunction with other approaches the information gained will certainly form an important part of an overall understanding of human behaviour. Man is a uniquely suitable subject for scientific investigation in that medical information of all kinds is continually being accumulated all over the world. In particular nearly 2000 different heritable disorders have now been identified.[4] This, in effect, represents a repository of about 2000 mutations in different genes. Many of these genes control basic metabolic processes or less obvious cellular mechanisms, but others specifically affect neurological functions. An essential point is that cells can be grown from individuals with a particular mutation (usually from a small skin biopsy, but cells from the brain can be grown post-mortem) and these can be compared with normal cells. In this way it is possible, in principle, to identify the biochemical defect in the affected individual by laboratory investigation. It is revealing, for example, that more is known about the repair of damaged DNA in man than in any other mammal, simply because the appropriate repair-deficient cell strains are available for study in the laboratory. There is not much doubt that mutations which produce neurological defects will be of inestimable value in unravelling the role of some normal genes which are required for brain structure and function. Although the cells available for study may not be initially neurones, it is not out of the question that it will in the future be possible to de-differentiate or re-differentiate cells grown in the laboratory into any cell type which is required for experimental investigation.

Fourth, an area of technology which has advanced at a rate comparable to molecular biology is that of electronics and computing. One of the most striking developments is the miniaturization of computer circuits. The analogy with brain function becomes obvious when very small computers can store and process very large amounts of information. There are, of course, fundamental differences in the way the brain and computers function. Computers are exceedingly fast and also very accurate. Brains function far more slowly and are not by any means always accurate. Computers rely on a simple binary code for the storage of information and are not at all adept at recognizing complex symbols, such as those making up language. A computer given information from a television camera could not easily distinguish two rather similar human faces. On the other hand, the human senses and brain are particularly good at recognizing and memorizing complex visual images, or patterns of sounds. In spite of these fundamental differences, few could doubt that the advances of computer technology will inevitably lead to insights into the various ways that information can be assimilated, stored and used by the brain. Of course computers are now being used all the time in modern research, including neurobiology. However, there is a basic difference between using a computer as a tool to analyse data and speed up experimental research, and using one as an actual model to mimic the complex circuitry of brain neurones. It is in this latter role that we can expect computers, in the hands of theoretical scientists, to make their most fundamental contribution to understanding brain function.

Fifth, a completely different approach to understanding human behaviour comes from the science of ethology. Charles Darwin was well aware of the importance of animal behaviour in evolution and he rightly perceived that it could be studied objectively by scientific methods.[5] Fifty or so years later the pioneering observations of animal behaviour by Konrad Lorenz, Julian Huxley, Niko Tinbergen, and Karl von Frisch established the foundations of the new science of ethology. I shall not attempt to review this field, even in the barest outline, but two of its fundamental features must be stressed. First, the animals are not manipulated experimentally: they may be sticklebacks in a tank, domesticated geese or jackdaws in the backyard, or animals of every kind in their natural environment. (This is to be contrasted with the completely different field of animal psychology; where animals are studied in the strictly artificial environment of a laboratory cage, often with the aid of complicated electronic or other equipment.)

Second, the observations which are made and recorded are as reproducible as in any other branch of experimental science. For example, if ethologist A describes in a publication the courtship behaviour of a particular species of animal, then ethologist B can go out into the field and be sure that in the same general environment he can make the same observations. That is *not* to say that ethology is an easy science; it critically depends on a particular skill in observation which allows the investigator to extract or simplify the crucial elements from what may appear at first sight a very complex jumble of behavioural activity. This is in sharp contrast to the rather random observations which are usually made by amateur naturalists or bird-watchers.

It is immediately evident that the principles of ethology are directly applicable to the study of human behaviour, because no experimental manipulation is involved. Initially, ethologists were cautious about this since they were as aware as anyone that man's behaviour depends on a complex inter-relationship between his genetic make-up and the cultural milieu in which he lives. However, caution now seems to have gone to the wind, and a large number of books have appeared in recent years which attempt to explain many aspects of human behaviour in ethological terms.[6] Many have, in my view, discredited the application of ethology to the study of man, since the authors do not distinguish between the interpretation of those aspects of human behaviour which can be directly related to those of primates or other mammals, from their own personal speculations about the basis of certain other features of human behaviour. Be that as it may, the point remains that ethology *is* directly applicable to the study of man and many valuable investigations have already been carried out, for instance, on the behaviour of human infants. In the future we can expect a comprehensive scientific discipline to emerge in which fact can be distinguished from fancy, and genetic components can be distinguished from cultural ones. Such a discipline will be an indispensable ingredient in the overall study of man and society.

For all the reasons I have mentioned in the last part of this chapter, I predict that scientific methods will be ultimately successful in unravelling the mysteries of the human brain.

This will necessarily tell us a great many things about human behaviour, about which we are at present ignorant. I shall return to this subject in Chapter 8.

# 6. Opposition to science

To deride the hope of progress is the ultimate fatuity, the
last word in poverty of spirit and meanness of mind.
P. B. Medawar[1]

My assessment of the likely future advances in molecular and
human biology presupposes that scientists will continue to
receive the necessary support and resources. There are, however, powerful pressure groups who in one way or another
would like to limit biological research. There is also a general
pessimism or loss of confidence in science, which contrasts
strongly with optimistic attitudes prevalent at the end of the
last century and the early decades of this one. It was then
widely assumed that the study of biology could in the long run
only be beneficial to mankind. That view is often now thought
to be naïve and out of date.

In this chapter I shall digress from my overall argument to
examine some of the hostile criticism or negative attitudes
towards modern biological science. First, I shall discuss some
of the specific fears people have and then consider more
generally the commonly held view that science is unable to
help solve basic human problems.

There is widespread antipathy to the prospect of scientists
manipulating genetic material or embryos. The cloning of
molecules, cells, or people in numerous fictional scenarios is
almost always associated with evil malpractice of one kind or
another. One source of concern is the ability to extract DNA
from cells of different species; cut it in pieces (with restriction
enzymes); rejoin sequences from different species; reinfect a
living micro-organism (usually the bacterium *Escherichia coli* or
a yeast); and then allow the new DNA to multiply during the
growth of these organisms. Some of the scientists who first used
this method pointed out that it might conceivably be dangerous
and that it should only be done under carefully controlled
conditions. This unleashed a blaze of publicity, a storm of
controversy, and a widespread view that the research could
result in the creation of dangerous pathogens, if not Franken-

stein monsters. The possibility that new combinations of DNA might be hazardous was originally a hypothesis and it remains a hypothesis.[2] There is no evidence of any kind that it is correct; indeed, evidence has accumulated that DNA is fragmented and reassorted under natural conditions and presumably this has been going on for thousands of millions of years. Moreover, there is now a much greater awareness that the random rejoining of DNA from different organisms is extremely unlikely to produce novel biological properties or phenotypes. Evolution by natural selection is a very slow process and proceeds one step at a time. The idea that huge jumps could be made in evolution simply because the DNA is in a laboratory test tube is certainly very naïve, if not a form of arrogance on the part of the scientists themselves. (This arrogance is illustrated by the popular phrase 'scientists playing God', which implies that transmutation of species is usually directed by a supernatural force, rather than natural selection, and that scientists themselves have harnessed this force.) Most molecular biologists now recognize that the original fears were exaggerated or unnecessary. Unfortunately, it will take much longer to reassure the public at large.

The second type of biological research which people strongly dislike is that involving the manipulation of eggs or embryos. For example, it is possible to remove the nucleus of an amphibian egg and replace it with another nucleus. In some cases normal, or fairly normal, development follows. If a group of identical donor nuclei are used, then a clone of offspring can be obtained from one mother. Similarly an early mammalian embryo with several cells might be dissociated into single cells and each implanted in one or more females. Again a clone of animals could then be produced. In other techniques two embryos can be fused, or one or a few cells can be transferred from one embryo to another. For reasons which are not altogether clear, this type of research arouses the strongest suspicions. It is felt that rich, powerful or influential people will in future clone themselves; or that the members of a human clone will be subjected to different environmental treatments, perhaps along the lines so graphically described by Aldous Huxley in *Brave new world*.

These fears are irrational and unfounded, for the following

reasons. It has been possible for a long time to carry out all kinds of experiments on human beings, but there is virtually unanimous agreement among doctors, scientists, and the public that this is not permissible, except in special, carefully controlled circumstances, such as the clinical trial to test the efficacy of a new treatment. There is no reason to believe that experiments on human embryos, of a type which can be carried out on toads or mice, would be in any way regarded differently from any other type of human experimentation. It should be noted that human clones already exist. Identical twins have the same genetic make-up and therefore constitute a 'mini-clone'. The situation could be exploited in all sorts of ways, for example, by placing twins in different carefully controlled environments to see what the effect would be on their personalities or intellectual development. To my knowledge, no one has suggested that this type of experiment should be done. (Of course, when identical twins have been separated for other reasons, they are studied by scientists and provide very important information about the relative contribution of genetic and environmental influences on the personality or other characteristics of the adult.) It is quite easy to change the genetic material of animals by traditional means, namely, artificial selection. In the domestic dog, which is just one species, size, shape, strength, colour, and particular skills have all been dramatically altered by selection. Endless variation of phenotype also exists in many other domesticated species. Presumably it would not be difficult to produce a similar variation in man, perhaps in the form of highly intelligent individuals, or supreme athletes, by selective breeding. So here is a technique for manipulating the human genotype which has existed for centuries, yet the possibility that it might be used is simply not worthy of discussion. Why, then, should the manipulation of human embryos be regarded as such a serious possibility? The usual argument is that if biologists or doctors in Hitler's regime could carry out experiments on human beings, then it is conceivable that a similar situation could arise today. The fallacy in the argument is that it fails to recognize that modern developmental biology is a sophisticated and international activity carried out by innumerable scientists who freely discuss and criticize each other's work. In such a situation the prospect of one scientist or laboratory hiding from the others in order to carry out secret nefarious research belongs only to the realm of science fiction. In fact people's worries have almost certainly been caused by the confusion between science fiction and reality: it is indeed often hard for the layman to tell whether a particular scenario is pure fantasy or whether it has real substance. Some writers have exploited this situation by claiming that certain experiments have already been carried out (such as the cloning of a man[3]), when they could not have in fact been done. It is unfortunate that some publishers, who should be in a position to obtain professional advice, cynically accept books of this type, because they know they will sell. It is not enough for scientists, who know the field, simply to deny the truth of the published claims. The remedy must be a much more fundamental one: a much better understanding of the reasons for the success of the scientific method; a much better knowledge of what is actually being done in biological laboratories and what will be done in the future; and a generally improved dialogue between scientists and non-scientists, which will change the grey areas of pseudo-science, science fiction and the like into a sharp boundary between concrete reality and pure fantasy.

I do not want to whitewash all biological research, or to give the impression that it is never hazardous. Returning to the genetics of micro-organisms, we know that a large number of experiments have been carried out with many dangerous bacteria or other pathogens, often in classified (i.e. secret) laboratories and in the name of 'defence' in biological warfare. This work has sometimes depended on the treatment of standard strains with potent mutagens to introduce genetic variation and it has also involved crosses between naturally occurring or artificially produced strains. Many genetic studies are also carried out in non-classified laboratories on pathogenic viruses. Although nowadays there is considerable concern about the safety of laboratory workers carrying out these experiments, the real possibility of danger does not seem to cause much concern, namely, that genetic studies on pathogens may result in the production of strains with completely new virulent properties, perhaps comparable to the virus causing myxomatosis in rabbits. A basic distinction should be made between the study of known strains of pathogens by the standard techniques

of microbiology, pathology, or biochemistry, and the introduction of new genetic variation in such pathogens, but this
does not seem to have been generally recognized.

Apart from some of the specific fears or suspicions people
have about manipulating, for example, DNA or embryos, there
is a much more general concern that the knowledge scientists
gain in the future will be in one way or another exploited or
misused. Scientists might become far too powerful and perhaps
adopt totalitarian attitudes to society. This view is, in large
part, based on the confusion between knowledge and power.
As I have explained, science is international and impersonal.
It advances as a result of cooperative activity. One of the
essential duties of a research scientist is to publish his results;
and once published this knowledge is, in effect, public property.
(I refer here to fundamental scientific research, not to classified
research in military establishments or applied research in
commercial laboratories.) The person who made the discovery
may have particular expertise, but since his methods are always
described in the publication, anyone else can, in principle,
repeat the work or extend it to a further stage. Society can
subsequently use the information which accumulates for good,
or possibly for bad ends, but the scientist at this stage is not in
any greater position of power than anyone else. Usually it is
governments or the representatives of governments who wield
power, just as they do in most other spheres of human activity.
Later on I shall argue that science will indeed transform
society, but it will not be the scientists themselves who impose
their will on anyone else. It will be the knowledge and information they gain which will undermine many of the established
traditions and also make it more and more difficult for people
to adopt dogmatic or prejudiced attitudes by hiding under a
cloak of ignorance.

In this context it is constructive to consider the demise of
religion in the United Kingdom and some other Western
nations. In medieval times and at other periods up until the
end of the nineteenth century, a majority of people accepted
without question the teaching of the Christian church. Bishops
and priests were very powerful influences in society, sometimes
by far the most powerful influence. If at these times, it had been
predicted that some time in the future the dogmas of the church

would be undermined and the power of the clergy go into rapid decline, the prediction would undoubtedly have been received with total disbelief. A society without a powerful church was inconceivable. Nevertheless, towards the end of the nineteenth century people's attitudes did begin to change. Christianity no longer has the all-pervading influence it used to enjoy. Now it merely expresses one viewpoint, among the many which exist in contemporary society. The advance of scientific rationalism, and particularly the Darwinian revolution, played a large part in reducing the power of the church. For similar reasons, we can predict the demise of certain political creeds in the future and this will necessarily result in a decline of the power of politicians as we know them today.

Sometimes a scientific theory is rejected simply because it is unpalatable, even though there may be overwhelming evidence in its favour. This response is an emotional one and it is the equivalent of burying one's head in the sand. The best example is evolution by natural selection: George Bernard Shaw, while accepting the validity of evolution, wrote:

. . . as compared with the open-eyed intelligent wanting and trying of Lamarck, the Darwinian process may be described as a chapter of accidents. As such, it seems simple, because you do not at first realise all that it involves. But when its whole significance dawns on you, your heart sinks into a heap of sand within you. There is a hideous fatalism about it, a ghastly and damnable reduction of beauty and intelligence, of strength and purpose, of honour and aspirations, to such casually picturesque changes as an avalanche may make in a mountain landscape, or a railway accident in a human figure.[4]

Many others have come to a similar conclusion, without expressing their feelings so graphically. In a sense, such an attitude represents a loss of nerve, an unwillingness to accept the reality of the world. The striking fact is that innumerable people come to exactly the opposite conclusion: that Darwinian natural selection brings meaning and sense into a living world which otherwise seems hopelessly complex and incomprehensible. The quotations of Francis Crick at the head of Chapter 4 illustrate the point with admirable brevity. The same situation applies to molecular biology as a whole. Many people so dislike the possibility that they may consist only of molecules that they simply reject it and maintain instead some kind of Cartesian dualism or vitalism. On the other hand many molecular biologists, including myself, find that the un-ravelling of the basic chemistry of life is enormously satisfying, not only on an intellectual level, but also on a personal or emotional one. This complex of discoveries is, in a word, life-enhancing.

I shall now consider the general argument that science, rather than being unlimited in its potential scope, has in fact quite well-defined limitations and for this reason cannot help mankind to solve the major problems it is confronted with. A common view is that moral judgements or value judgements depend on our inner conscience and that they cannot be under-stood or analysed in scientific terms. Nevertheless, such judge-ments are never made in a vacuum since external influences are also important; each factor has to be taken into account before a choice, decision or judgement is made. It is far easier to make a value judgement if knowledge or information is available about the situation in question and the consequences of each possible course of action. I shall illustrate this with a number of specific examples in the following chapter. Of course, it often happens that there is little or no guiding information and that we have then to rely only on an inner conscience, but that is not to say that in these instances information would be of no use to us.

It is also possible to take the view that the existence of knowledge does not necessarily lead to appropriate action. The problem is not lack of information, but man's inability to use it properly. Thus it would be possible now to eradicate much disease and starvation in many parts of the world, but those countries with the necessary resources to do it do not act. The problem becomes one of politics or economics rather than of science. Nevertheless, if scientific advances had not been made at all, it would not even be possible in principle to begin to eradicate these diseases. A vital prerequisite is to make the necessary study of pathogens, insect vectors, the ecology of disease transmission, and so on. A solution can then be defined on which the World Health Organization or other bodies can act. Without expertise, nothing at all could be achieved.

One of the assumptions I make in this book is that all aspects of human activity are part and parcel of man's biological make-up and that they can therefore be studied by scientific methods.

This will shock people who believe that certain domains of human inquiry and creativity are outside science and can never be studied by objective scientific criteria. For example, artistic activity, whether it be literature, music, painting, or sculpture, is usually thought to be necessarily a personal and subjective experience, both for the creator and the individuals who respond to it. However, there can be no valid reason why all this activity should not be regarded as part of man's biological make-up. In this book, I occasionally invoke a hypothetical observer from outer space, who has such supreme scientific ability that he can successfully study and understand all aspects of man, including his behaviour. Would not the activity of artists and the way people react to the arts be fair game to him? Would it not be possible for him to discover why a certain piece of music was frequently performed and enthusiastically received, while some other piece put together with equal effort by its composer, had no similar effect on its audience? To understand this would not only involve a comprehensive study of man's auditory apparatus, but a great many other aspects of his brain function. Very likely it would also require an understanding of the musical influences to which he was subjected in the society in which he found himself and probably many other influences as well. If this conclusion is correct, then there is the further question of the desirability of man himself obtaining this information. Many people feel that objectively studying something as personal as art will necessarily debase it. It is believed that the inquisitive scientists will take the pleasure out of the infinite richness of human activity by scrutinizing it, analysing it, and reducing it to basic principles. This is a myth. Physicists do not respond to rainbows differently from people who do not understand how they are formed. Indeed, it is possible that their appreciation of them is enhanced. Knowledge of the exact frequency of all the notes in a piece of music does not spoil our pleasure. Could it be possibly said that botanists or geologists enjoy a landscape less than other people because they understand something about the trees or the rock formations within it? If scientific inquiry does not interfere with human activities such as these, does it in any way enhance them? If not, why bother to undertake the investigation in the first place? I shall return to these questions later on and shall try to explain why, for example, an objective understanding of art and aesthetics may be of great importance.

It is unfortunate that many people are so committed to a certain point of view (often on the flimsiest of grounds) that they positively resent the prospect of a proper scientific investigation. On the one hand, they feel that their own freedom of action may be curtailed and on the other they are worried that the scientists themselves will dictate a particular course of action. This attitude is regrettable from all points of view. In the first place, people should not be so confident about their own opinions, if these are based on inadequate information. Second, the existence of information should enable them to have a more valid opinion or make a better judgement than was possible before. Third, the scientist is no different from any other member of the public; he is instrumental in obtaining information, but he has to make up his mind about any course of action in the same way as anyone else.

It can be maintained that the very richness of human life is due to the diversity of opinions which persist in human society. But is it possible to believe that the inquisitive scientist, by probing and analysing human behaviour, will destroy some of this richness, because freedom of action and belief will be curtailed? I do not think so, since the acquisition and transmission of experience and knowledge is the fundamental feature of man, which has allowed him to evolve complex and sophisticated societies. To deny the further pursuit of this basic human tradition, because it might interfere with 'the richness of life' epitomizes the poverty of mind and the meanness of spirit to which P. B. Medawar refers in the quotation at the head of this chapter. Who could claim that the ignorant and mis-informed lead a more worth-while existence than those who try to investigate and understand every aspect of human life?

# 7. Making decisions

Exact knowledge is the enemy of controversy.[1]

IN Chapter 5 I reviewed some of the advances we can expect in the future in the study of the biology of man. I shall now return to the present and the recent past and examine some of the effects existing biological and especially medical knowledge has had on human welfare. In numerous instances this knowledge has been acted upon in a rational and sensible way. People's lives have often been changed for the better, because knowledge has replaced ignorance, superstition, or blind prejudice. Accurate information about a particular disease has frequently led to the development of a specific and successful treatment, and the application of this treatment has become totally non-controversial. Hence the dictum at the head of this chapter: exact knowledge is the enemy of controversy. In this and the following chapter I shall argue that exact knowledge will extend in the future to more and more domains of human activity, including human social behaviour itself. This exact knowledge will also be acted on in an increasingly rational and sensible way, because controversy will progressively diminish.

Leaving aside techniques of surgery, the study of medicine can be conveniently divided into three main phases. In the first phase, the pathogens which cause many diseases were identified. In the nineteenth century there were pioneering studies on bacterial infections and this has been followed up more recently by the identification of many infectious viruses. At the same time pathogenic protozoa and other animal parasites have been intensively studied. Infectious disease can in general be treated by four methods. (1) The pathogen can simply be removed from the environment by improving hygiene. Once the micro-organism is identified and the pathways of transmission understood, it becomes possible, in numerous instances, to take steps to diminish the likelihood of infection. (2) Vaccines can be prepared from pathogens or their structural components and used to immunize people against infection. Such vaccines can be quite cheap to manufacture and very large numbers of people can therefore be treated. The existence of a majority of immunized people leads to a decline in the population of the infectious organism and in some instances, such as smallpox, to the virtual eradication of the disease. (3) Many chemicals have been screened for their lethal effects on an invading pathogen. Some have been discovered which act fairly specifically against the infecting bacterium or protozoan, while having no serious toxic effects on the individual being treated. (4) A special class of naturally occurring chemicals are the antibiotics. These are highly specific and effective in their action on bacteria and in many cases have no deleterious effect at all on people. They have revolutionized the treatment of infectious disease. Chemical agents which specifically act on viral pathogens have not been discovered, although the use of certain proteins produced by mammalian cells, collectively called interferon, has considerable promise.

Taken together, these treatments have been outstandingly successful in removing most of the lethal diseases of man and raising his expectation of life enormously. The application of the knowledge gained is still a great problem in many parts of the world, but with regard to the research itself it can be said that it is nearing completion.

The second phase of medical research is concerned with what we can conveniently label *intrinsic diseases*. These are due to defects or faults in the basic biochemical properties of cells. They may arise spontaneously (i.e. without known cause), or because there are dangerous chemical or physical agents (such as radiation) in the environment in which people live. Alternatively a biochemical defect may be inherited from one or both parents. Cancer is one of the most prevalent intrinsic diseases and there is much evidence suggesting that a high proportion of all cases is due to exposure to environmental agents, most of which, however, remain unidentified. As I have previously mentioned, there are a very large number of inherited diseases in man, although fortunately most of them are extremely rare. Some of the more common ones such as muscular dystrophy or cystic fibrosis are the subject of intensive research. The overall study of inherited diseases in man will keep biochemists and geneticists busy for a very long time to come. Also in the category of intrinsic disease are those which lead to degenerative changes in particular tissues, for instance, multiple sclerosis or rheumatoid arthritis. The latter is a possible example of an autoimmune disease, where the body's own defence against invading organisms is for some reason turned against some of its own cells or tissues. The process of ageing itself leads to a particular spectrum of pathologies, especially the cardiovascular diseases, which are the commonest cause of death today. Ageing also frequently results in the decline of brain function (senile dementia) or in the impairment of vision and hearing. Defects in nutrition can also be included in the general category of intrinsic disease. An understanding of the biochemistry and physiology of living cells and tissues has revealed the basic nutritional requirements of human beings. This has made it possible to combat many deficiency diseases, although unfortunately they remain a major health problem in many Third World countries.

The third phase of biomedical research will not be concerned with the body as such, but with all aspects of abnormal or antisocial human behaviour. The malaise which affects societies as a whole, or individuals within societies, is the greatest problem to be faced in the future. Everywhere we see stress and strife; violence and aggression; depression and breakdown, together with conflict, exploitation, and acquisitive behaviour. All this can occur within individual societies. The tensions between different societies or different countries lead to a far more threatening malaise—the prospect of war and the use of weapons of mass destruction. A common view is that the study and understanding of these aspects of human activity is the province of psychology, psychiatry, sociology, or other human sciences. Perhaps an even commoner one is that these problems are completely outside science, and that they can be dealt with only by political means or merely by an improvement in 'moral' attitudes. These viewpoints may well be valid now, but in the future a complete understanding of human behaviour and the way people interact with each other, and with the environment in general, must necessarily provide insight into the origin or cause of many of the problems man faces today. The study of the human nervous system will initiate the third phase of biomedical research. This research will unravel many aspects of human behaviour about which we are at present completely ignorant. This will be the topic of my next chapter. In the remainder of this one I shall try to demonstrate the positive way in which people have in general reacted to the first and second phases of biomedical research. I shall argue that when information becomes available which is of specific benefit to an individual or the society as a whole, then it is usually gratefully accepted. Although there are many areas of controversy in the practice of medicine today, there are also innumerable examples of particular treatments, remedies, or preventative measures, which are no longer controversial. I shall review a selection of these and also mention some examples of diseases at present incurable in humans, which will be treated in the future without controversy once research has provided the means to do this. Finally, I shall discuss more generally the constructive attitudes society now seems to have when confronted with individuals who are either physically handicapped or who have for one reason or another developed antisocial behaviour.

Let me begin with some simple examples. When it was discovered earlier in this century that certain vitamins were essential for normal growth and body maintenance, steps were taken to supplement diets which were deficient in particular vitamins. For example, a child suffering from rickets was provided with foods rich in vitamin D or a supply of the purified form. If any parent had objected to this remedy, their reaction would have been regarded as abnormal. The facts about nutritional needs became fully known to the public in the Second World War, when rationing was introduced. In spite of the limited food available, the overall health of children actually improved, because they were, in many cases, obtaining a properly balanced diet for the first time in their lives. Nowadays almost everyone realizes that diet must contain certain components, even though the underlying chemistry of nutrition is to most people a closed book. In some cases special diets are necessary. For instance, if it is discovered that an individual has an unusually high level of cholesterol in his blood, then he can avoid foods which contain cholesterol. In the case of a hormone deficiency, such as diabetes, the appropriate quantity of insulin can be administered. In these and many other similar cases it would be surprising if the individual concerned did not accept the situation and, under medical supervision, administer the remedy himself.

In some cases an inborn error of metabolism may lead to severe body malfunction, but this can be prevented, in large part, by special diet. The best-known example is the inherited disease phenylketonuria, which is present in about one in ten thousand births. If untreated, it leads to severe mental retardation, but it can be easily diagnosed by a simple chemical test on a small sample of blood. Any child affected must then be given a special diet free of the amino acid phenylalanine. In order to treat the very small fraction of children with the disease, it is necessary for all children to be tested, and this is accepted by almost all parents.

Prevention of infectious disease by inoculation is almost universally approved. The world-wide vaccination of children against smallpox has led to the virtual elimination of the disease. How many individuals failed or refused to respond to the ready availability of Sabin or Salk polio vaccines? Concerted action abolished the disease in the United Kingdom and elsewhere. Of course, it is sometimes necessary to balance the very slight risk of inoculation against the protection it provides. Inoculation against whooping cough is a case in point. A minority of parents may refuse the treatment for their children, but if the majority accept it, then the incidence of the disease will decline.

The example of genetic counselling is illuminating. Individuals may be the carriers of a genetic disease without showing any visible manifestation of it, that is, they have a genetic defect on a chromosome inherited from one of their parents, but this is recessive, i.e. it is masked by a normal gene on the corresponding chromosome from the other parent. They can then seek advice about the probability of their own children having the disease. Often this is done after one affected child has already been born. In such cases the genetic counsellor will provide the necessary information, but he never dictates to the parents what they should or should not do. (In the example I have mentioned there may be a 25 per cent chance that any child will express the disease, and a 50 per cent chance that a child will carry the disease.) In such situations, parents may have absolutely no knowledge of science or genetics and yet this does not in any way prevent them from making sensible decisions about what they should do. They may, for example, decide to adopt children, rather than have their own. Alternatively, it may be possible to screen the foetus for the presence of the inherited disease using the procedure known as amniocentesis. In this technique cells found in the amniotic fluid of the foetus are removed as early as possible in pregnancy and are grown in the laboratory and then examined for chromosome or biochemical abnormalities. The number of individual centres which provide this diagnostic service has increased enormously in recent years and so has the number of inherited diseases which can be identified by laboratory tests. Some of these tests may involve very elaborate techniques in molecular biology. For example, the disease thalassemia, which leads to haemoglobin deficiency, can be identified by the absence of a specific sequence of DNA in the chromosomes. Other tests are far more straightforward; Down's syndrome (mongolism) is a case in point. The incidence of mongolism increases sharply with the age of the mother. Amniocentesis is frequently carried out on older pregnant women, and diagnosis simply involves counting the number of chromosomes of the foetal cells. Confirmation that the foetus is afflicted with the genetic defect can then be followed by abortion, assuming that that is the wish of the parents. The fact that this very effective means of preventing the birth of many abnormal children is being increasingly used shows that many parents accept it. If most rejected the use of the technique, there would be no basis for setting up the appropriate clinics and laboratories. There are also environmental factors which are likely to produce abnormalities in children. Infection with German measles during pregnancy is one and women who know the risk usually decide to have an abortion. Of course, there are strong pressure groups who oppose abortion under any circumstances. To make their case they use various forms of propaganda or persuasion. For example, they may glorify parents who courageously struggle to bring up children with severe abnormalities, such as spina bifida. Nevertheless, the number of mothers who choose amniocentesis and the possibility of abortion increases all the time. There is no element of persuasion involved because they are making their own decision. They are also collaborating, in their own way, in an overall programme to eliminate one of the most serious of the remaining human diseases, that is, the total aggregate of inherited abnormalities.

In recent years there has been an explosion of concern about the various forms of environmental pollution. More specifically, people have become aware of their exposure to chemical or physical agents (carcinogens) which can cause cancer. There are now much stricter safety regulations than there used to be about the distribution of these agents in the factory or home environment. People do not have to be knowledgeable about the way such chemicals interact with and damage DNA in order to be concerned about their effects. Of course, there are pressure groups who profit from the sale of dangerous products and try to override public concern in one way or another. The best example of this is the advertisement and sale of cigarettes. At first sight, this provides a striking exception to the argument I have been making, namely, that when medical knowledge is made available, people will in general accept its validity and respond in a rational way. In spite of the establishment of a direct link between cigarette smoking and lung cancer (as well as some other diseases) the consumption of cigarettes has not declined. More important, the proportion of young people who take up smoking seems to be as high as ever. There is strong social pressure on young people to do this, because it is regarded as part and parcel of the process of becoming an adult. Moreover, smoking is addictive, which makes it particularly difficult to discontinue the habit. There are also powerful vested interests which act against the abolition of smoking. Governments, which receive so much tax from sales, have never made any serious attempt to get the facts across to the public, in spite of continual pressure from the medical profession. Although most people may be aware of the potential danger of smoking, I suspect they have no clear knowledge of the nature of the evidence or the frequency of lung cancer in life-long heavy smokers. It is a striking fact that the incidence of smoking among professional groups has declined in recent years and this must surely be due to their greater awareness of the nature and degree of the hazard. There is not much doubt that the discovery of an equivalent carcinogenic effect in a dispensable food additive, for example, would lead to the banning of that additive with a minimum of delay.

The widespread concern about irresponsible use of dangerous chemicals seems to come from the realization that intrinsic diseases are now the most important problem in medicine. Powerful pressure groups tried to discount the effect of thalidomide on unborn children. In the end they were forced to accept the established fact that thalidomide is teratogenic and pay heavy compensation to the victims who had been exposed to it. Spina bifida is a crippling disorder which is due to defective development of the foetus. It has often been suggested that this is due to a teratogenic chemical in the food of the pregnant woman, or possibly a lack of essential components in the diet. If this were the case and the cause were identified, steps would be taken to prevent pregnant women receiving a faulty diet, even if this was inconvenient or expensive.

Although science cannot claim credit for the widespread use of traditional methods of birth control, the development of the more effective oral contraceptive was the direct result of basic research on the structure and function of sex hormones. The speed with which this method was adopted by women was remarkable. It provides a clear example of the way people's lives can be changed beneficially by voluntary acceptance of the results of biomedical research: effective birth control liberates women from the burden of endless child-bearing and child-rearing. Although some men might object to the use of any future male contraceptive pill, a great many would undoubtedly accept it. In many countries the population explosion predicted a few years ago has not materialized. This is in many cases due to the spread of effective means of birth control, especially the pill. Thus, not only are individual's lives transformed by the acceptance of this method, but communities as a whole also benefit enormously.

The various stresses of modern society all too often lead to mental breakdown. More than one in ten of all the adults in the United Kingdom have at one time or another received psychiatric advice, treatment, or have spent time in mental hospitals. N. S. Sutherland has published an account of his own experience and, as a professional psychologist, has provided an illuminating and objective review of the various schools of psychiatry, or psychoanalysis, and the treatments which are recommended.[2] They are far from satisfactory. This is an area which seems to consist of a mixture of empirical knowledge, inspired guesswork, common sense, dogmatic assertion, and the use of chemical or physical treatments, the physiological basis of which is usually totally obscure. The situation is entirely unsatisfactory and it is a consequence of our extremely limited knowledge of the human mind and the structure and function of the human brain. But who could doubt that a really effective treatment for mental illness would not be avidly accepted? More specifically, certain mental illnesses, such as schizophrenia, may have a relatively simple chemical basis. If so, and if the chemistry were understood, the prospects of effective treatment would be immeasurably greater.

The attitude of the public to mental illness is totally different from what it was, say, a hundred years ago. Affected people were then hidden away in 'lunatic asylums' and parents with mentally defective children were often ashamed of them and kept them out of sight. At the present time there is far more compassion, sympathy, and understanding. It is not completely clear why this change in attitude has occurred, but it is almost certainly related to a general understanding that mental illness must have a physical basis, and that it is not due, for instance, to the sins of the parents or the intervention of supernatural evil forces. Down's syndrome or mongolism is an example where the cause has been identified: it is due to the inheritance of an additional small chromosome. The fact that this is a chance genetic event clearly makes a great difference to public attitudes to affected children. Not only parents, but large sections of the public believe that such children should receive special training, which is often expensive, in order to achieve maximum development of their potential ability. This policy extends to many types of mentally retarded children or to those who are 'maladjusted' to their family or the society around them. Indeed, in many cases much more attention is paid to the welfare or treatment of such individuals than to the education and training of children within the normal range of ability. This must surely mean that, given the opportunity, steps would always be taken to prevent the cause of the particular mental disturbance. Suppose for example, a specific environ-

mental factor was clearly identified which led to a maladjusted condition. Can any one doubt that great care would
then be taken to avoid this deleterious influence?

In general, there is more understanding of the problems of
imprisonment than there used to be. In the past prison was
regarded largely as a form of punishment or retribution and, of
course, that is still a common view. There is, however, an increasing awareness that many antisocial acts which result in
people being sent to prison are not just due to wilful behaviour
or sinfulness; they are the results of complex interactions in
which social and genetic factors may be involved. There is
evidence that men with two Y sex-chromosomes have a significantly greater tendency to indulge in violent crime than men
with normal chromosomes.[3] If crime in such cases is related to
a genetic abnormality of this type, it is absurd to think in terms
of prison as a punishment or retribution. To put it another way,
if behaviour is determined by intrinsic and extrinsic factors,
rather than being based on free will, then punishment *per se*
becomes irrelevant. It should be clearly recognized that a
penalty is no more than a deterrent. In spite of some vociferous
elements in society who demand more stringent punishment
for offenders, in general there seems to be an increasing measure
of agreement that antisocial behaviour is largely a product of
the defects in society itself and emphasis should be placed on
the reform or rehabilitation of prisoners. We have moved a
long way from some of the barbaric practices of the past (but
which, unfortunately, still persist in some parts of the world)
and this must be due to a wider realization of the fact that every
individual is the product of his genotype and the environment
in which he finds himself. More real information about the
causes of antisocial or violent behaviour, including, for
example, soccer hooliganism and vandalism, can only lead to
a more rational and objective attitude among the public at
large and this would go along with the desire to remove the
causes of this behaviour.

In the past the intellectual superiority of men over women
was assumed, and this is still the case in many parts of the world.
The liberation of women from this position of inferiority can at
least in part be attributed to the information which has accumulated over the years about the very similar intelligence and

intellectual ability of both sexes. It is no longer possible to discriminate against women when it can be plainly demonstrated that in very many fields of human activity they perform just as well as men. It is not only a question of making judgements about human rights, but also a matter of documenting this close similarity in performance. It would be immeasurably harder to argue the case for women's liberation if this documentation did not exist. This is yet another example of knowledge superseding controversy.

In this chapter I have not referred to the bread and butter of medical practice, but concentrated on those topics in which patients, relatives, or others concerned are put in the position of choosing between a particular recommended treatment and some other course of action. It goes without saying that much of the time medical treatment is scarcely a matter of choice. Anyone suffering from appendicitis is hardly likely to refuse an operation; anyone dying from loss of blood after a car accident will not refuse a blood transfusion; anyone with a broken limb will want to have it set properly. (I am ignoring certain religious minorities who for one reason or another refuse to accept medical treatment.) I deliberately selected examples involving choice to emphasize the point that people do, on the whole, make sensible decisions about their own or their relatives' health and welfare. In many cases they are making value judgements. Given the evidence from amniocentesis that a foetus is a mongol (because its cells have 47 rather than the normal 46 chromosomes), the parents have to decide whether to have the child or to have it aborted. This is a value judgement, but the choice is between two fairly well-defined consequences. On accepting the amniocentesis procedure, they are committing themselves to the necessity of having to make that choice. But the crucial factor in the situation is to first establish whether or not the foetus has a normal complement of chromosomes. Exact knowledge is needed, before the choice can be made. Most of the other examples I gave also involve value judgements, but often the choice between two courses of action is very much easier than the example of abortion. In general, when information is made available to people who are not particularly knowledgeable about the underlying science, the response is as sensible as that made by experts in the field in question. People's lives have obviously been changed in all sorts of ways as a result of the advances in medical sciences. Most of these changes have been beneficial and have been willingly accepted by the public. However, changes are not in any real sense controlled by the public. They occur because certain knowledge accumulates, and, in a sense, people are overtaken by events, without being fully aware of what is happening.

This may sound ominous, but it is not, because in all cases people are free to accept or reject a particular course of action. There is no coercion involved. Society even allows a Jehovah's Witness to refuse the blood transfusion which would save a child's life. The procedure of 'mass medication' which eliminates freedom of choice is unacceptable to many people. This is almost certainly the reason why fluoridation of drinking water has not been generally implemented in the United Kingdom in spite of the compelling evidence that the effect in preventing tooth decay would be dramatic. Nevertheless, in most instances, people adopt a rational position and accept the information and expert advice which is available to them.

I have so far said very little about the role of practising doctors or physicians. They are in effect intermediaries between the patient and the research laboratory. They should be communicators who explain the health problem, understand the cause, and prescribe possible remedies. Unfortunately they do not always communicate very well. The public at large tends to regard them as experts, which they are not, and the doctors themselves are often too prone to revert to a formidable jargon, or may not even try to explain at all the medical or biological aspects of the illness or disease. Also, they are not always aware of recent developments in biomedical research, although it is part of their job to be well informed. They are too prone to refer patients to specialists and they are also too willing to dispense new drugs proffered by pharmaceutical companies. In many cases these have never been shown to be effective or, even worse, have never been properly tested for dangerous side-effects, as in the example of the teratogenic effect of thalidomide.

In spite of all this, the system seems to work, since the overall standard of health in the community at large does improve. It seems to work because by and large there is considerable respect for the achievements of medical science in the last hundred years or so. The channels of communication are adequate, because doctors are a reasonably effective intermediary between the laboratory scientist and general public. In fields of biology which are not yet within medicine, the intermediary does not exist and in consequence there is widespread confusion and misunderstanding about the advances scientists are making. Of course, the situation in medicine is far from perfect: sometimes treatment is provided by specialists which has disastrous consequences. The operation to sever the connections to the frontal lobes of the brain is one notorious example. Another cruel and ineffective procedure, without any scientific basis, was the attempt to treat schizophrenia by inducing repeated muscular convulsions and comas with injections of excess doses of insulin.[2] In general, the medical profession is much more willing to use new treatments with a 'scientific' label than it is to try some of the traditional remedies offered by the supporters of 'fringe medicine'. The public is also not blameless, as the example of smoking and lung cancer shows. There is certainly plenty of room for improvement in the theory and practice of medicine at all levels.

Nevertheless, few people doubt that advances will continue to be made in the study of intrinsic diseases. There are formidable problems ahead in finding effective treatments for cancer and many inherited diseases, but it would be surprising if they were not eventually solved. I now wish to look further ahead than that, at the problems which beset societies as a whole, and at the problem of human nature itself. I believe that the proper study of mankind is that of man and that the way to obtain the information we need about ourselves is by investing far greater resources in the pursuit of biological knowledge at all levels.

# 8. Human behaviour

In a sense, human genes have surrendered their primacy in human evolution to an entirely new non-biological or superorganic agent, culture. However, it should not be forgotten that this agent is entirely dependent on the human genotype.

Th. Dobzhansky[1]

## I: The present

DURING the period when genetics, biochemistry, and molecular biology were so successful, psychology and the social sciences were struggling to establish a coherent, cohesive body of knowledge about man himself. Why should overall progress in these fields be so lamentably slow? It is certainly not due to lack of enthusiasm or interest on the part of the public. Ever since Freudian psychoanalytical theory burst upon the world, there has been unbounded encouragement for the human sciences as a whole. Educated people who would never claim to understand the physical or biological sciences are expected to be knowledgeable in the various theories of psychology. Numerous books written by psychologists or sociologists sell very widely and are read by professionals and non-professionals alike. There is an extraordinary faith in the efficacy of psychoanalysis, or other psychiatric methods, particularly in the United States, and an enormous amount of money is spent, in one way or another, on this branch of medicine. At the same time there is widespread research in psychology and related sciences in universities, institutes, or medical schools. Sociology became one of the most popular and sought after courses in many of the newly established universities in the United Kingdom. From all this, we can conclude that there is a general awareness of the extreme importance of the study of the human mind and of human social behaviour. There is also a widespread belief that advances are continually taking place in the fields of experimental psychology, psychiatry, sociology, social anthropology, moral philosophy, and so on. The common view is that professional investigators in these and related fields of research are using scientific objective methods and therefore progress will inevitably occur. Why then is there a struggle to establish a solid corpus of exact knowledge?

The reasons are not too hard to see. In the previous chapter I pointed out the obvious, that the human brain is by far the most complex biological object available for study on this planet and that therefore it will be the last to be understood. From the point of view of the professional biologist, it seems unreasonable to try to get information about the structure and function of the human brain, when so little is yet known about the central nervous system of even the simplest animals. Therefore psychology and the other fields I have mentioned are in a sense trying to make short cuts. Their work is based on the view that real progress can be made by methods which do not involve studies at the cellular or biochemical level. After about eighty years of research, there does not seem very much evidence that these short cuts are leading anywhere. This is not to deny that a mass of extremely useful and important information has been accumulated from well planned investigations, and it is well known that many of the results obtained are scrutinized and assessed for their significance by the application of rigorous statistical procedures. The basic problem has been to fit all this information into a consistent and comprehensive theory of human behaviour.

This brings me to a second reason for slow progress. The pioneering and influential work of Sigmund Freud was almost immediately followed by a schism which led to separate branches of psychoanalytical theory propounded by C. G. Jung and A. Adler. Since that time quite different schools of psychological thought have emerged, several of which have totally rejected the validity of the procedures and theory of the psychoanalysts. I do not intend to review these here; it is sufficient for my argument to state that they do indeed present conflicting viewpoints or interpret known observations in quite different ways. No science can make consistent progress when professionals in the field cannot agree on the interpretation of data and when each school of thought formulates its own set of hypotheses. Moreover in psychology, hypotheses are often so ill-defined, or so all-embracing, that they do not make

specific testable predictions. According to Popper's definition,
theories are part of science only if they make predictions which
are in principle refutable by observation or experiment. In the
general field of human behaviour, theories can very often be
modified or adapted to fit any particular observation. Popper
cites an interesting example in his book *Conjectures and refutations*.

The Freudian analysts emphasised that their theories were constantly verified
by their 'clinical observations'. As for Adler, I was much impressed by a
personal experience. Once, in 1919, I reported to him a case which to me did
not seem particularly Adlerian, but which he found no difficulty in analysing
in terms of his theory of inferiority feelings, although he had not even seen the
child. Slightly shocked I asked him how he could be so sure. 'Because of my
thousandfold experience', he replied; whereupon I could not help saying:
'And with this new case, I suppose, your experience has become thousand-
and-one-fold'.[2]

Popper has often pointed out that the secret of the enormous
appeal of various theories in psychology lay in their ability to
explain everything. This being so, there is the danger that they
may come to resemble political or religious dogmas rather than
remaining within the province of science. It is no accident that
so many schools of thought exist in the general field of human
psychology: when solid information is so hard to come by
there are necessarily a large number of alternative interpreta-
tions. It is also revealing that the most important solid advances
in the area of psychology and psychiatry have been based on
empirical methods. For example, experimental psychology has
yielded a great deal of important information about the pathways and patterns of sensory perception. In clinical psychiatry,
the beneficial effects of many drugs are not in dispute, even
though the biochemical or neurological basis of their action is
not yet known. In an earlier chapter I emphasized that the
information at present available about the structure and
function of the central nervous system would eventually be
assimilated into a description of the whole system. In the same
way, the existing information in the fields of psychology, social
anthropology, and sociology and so on, will become just one
part of a total understanding of the behavioural make-up of
man.

In addition to this there is the unique insight into the human
condition which is provided by literature in all its forms. The
underlying nature of man and the endless variation of human

behaviour has also been the major preoccupation of poets, novelists, and playwrights. The literary critic F. R. Leavis maintained that the importance of literature was to help people make correct judgements about their own or other people's lives.[3] And the psychologist N. S. Sutherland has remarked that students who wish to understand human nature itself would do better to read the great writers than to study psychology.[4] Nevertheless no one could claim that literature can possibly provide a complete account of human behaviour.

Traditionally, the social sciences have made the tacit or implicit assumption that most individuals are to all intents and purposes the same in their genetic make-up and that the variation we see in the behaviour of individuals, and in the way different societies are organized, is very largely the result of environmental or cultural factors. Also, by and large, they have not considered the evolutionary origins of man and human societies. For these reasons, certain biologists felt they could usefully contribute to discussion in the areas of psychology, social anthropology, sociology, moral philosophy or political theory. In particular, E. O. Wilson has been a strong advocate of the study of sociobiology.[5] This new field originates on the one hand from the scientific study of animal behaviour, particularly the social behaviour of a wide range of species, and on the other from the knowledge that all this behaviour evolved by Darwinian natural selection. Convincing explanations of the evolution of many types of behaviour in animals have recently been forthcoming: for example, sexual, aggressive, altruistic, or maternal behaviour. Man's own patterns of behaviour must be related to the hunter–gatherer existence he led during his evolution from primate ancestors; subsequently his evolution was largely cultural, but this was itself the product of his genetic make-up or genotype. (The genes inherited from parents constitute the genotype. This must be distinguished from the phenotype, which is the collection of characteristics actually expressed in an individual and is the product of both the genotype and environmental influences.) Sociobiologists believe that if the scientific study of the genetic factors which influence human behaviour is combined with the more traditional methods used by psychologists and social scientists, then a new illuminating synthesis will emerge. In his book *On human nature*, E. O. Wilson writes 'Science may soon be in a position to investigate the very origin and meaning of human values, from which all ethical pronouncements and much of political practice flow.'[6] The crucial word in this quotation is 'soon'. The sociobiologists are in danger of falling into the same trap as the psychologists; they may be trying to take short cuts and they are formulating an overall view of human behaviour which is in principle capable of explaining everything. More and more of the properties of human societies, including religion itself, become explicable in terms of the genetic factors which conferred adaptive advantage, in the Darwinian sense, during the evolution of man. That is not to say that sociobiologists believe that cultural differences are genetically determined; they attempt to explain the origin of the cultural features of human societies in genetic terms. The sociobiological or adaptationist approach has been heavily criticized, for example, in the amusing and penetrating article by S. J. Gould and R. C. Lewontin called 'The spandrels of San Marco and the Panglossian paradigm: a critique of the adaptationist programme'.[7] Their basic point is that the mere existence of a particular anatomical feature, or pattern of behaviour, in an organism does not mean that it is a positive evolutionary adaptation.

My own view is that the basic premise of the sociobiologists is quite correct, namely that man can only be understood in terms of his evolutionary origins, but that much of the speculation, interesting though it is, is untestable and therefore outside science. I also think they are absurdly optimistic in believing that very important questions about human behaviour will soon be answered by any 'new synthesis' provided by sociobiology. My main argument is that these answers *will* eventually be forthcoming, but only after we have unravelled the structure and function of the human brain.

It is a depressing aspect of human behaviour itself that the absence of precise and well-documented information does not in the least inhibit people from adhering to political views, theories or opinions with the most fervent intensity and dogmatism. We do not find that those who belong to religious or political groups are fond of conceding that their opinions could be totally mistaken. Unfortunately, the same is all too often true in areas which are commonly regarded as belonging to the scientific study of man.

## II: The future

In the second part of this chapter I shall start with the assumption that we have at present no exact knowledge about the inward or outward forces which govern human behaviour. I wish to avoid expressing any personal opinions except to reiterate that the human behavioural phenotype is amenable to scientific investigation and that in future more and more information will become available. It will be futile as well as presumptuous to try to guess the nature of this knowledge. But it does seem to be reasonable to enumerate some areas of ignorance which could in my opinion, be eventually replaced by areas of knowledge. My aim is to argue that when this information is gained it cannot fail to be of the greatest significance to all the members of human societies.

Unfortunately, the listing of areas of ignorance is necessarily controversial, because any reader who has a firm belief or opinion about a particular aspect of human behaviour will not admit ignorance about it. Moreover, he will almost always be able to find support in that particular subset of books or monographs which support his own point of view. There are indeed enormous numbers of publications which cover in one way or another the various fields of human activity I shall mention. Many are reputable and scholarly works, but I maintain that none of them provide real answers to the crucial questions we can ask about human behaviour. There may be very interesting theories, speculations and ideas, as well as much documentation of facts, but this is not at all the same as the exact knowledge we have, for instance, in the field of molecular biology. In using the word 'ignorance', I mean that this type of knowledge is absent. I cannot expect general acceptance of this, simply because many people, such as Marxists or Christians, are convinced that answers to many of the questions one can ask about man and society are already available.

It is convenient to begin with the old controversy about the relative contributions of genetic and environmental factors in shaping human personalities and determining their intellectual capacity and achievement. The first point is that the controversy is in large part artificial. Geneticists have known for decades that the phenotype of an organism is the product of *both* the inherited genes and the environment in which the organism finds itself. If essential genes are absent or altered then normal development is impossible. Similarly normal genes cannot support development of the organism if the environment is deficient. This interdependence of genetic and environmental factors can be easily understood by the analogy of the farmer's field. The shape of the field is not very important to the farmer, but its area certainly is. Imagine a rectangular field, where one dimension is viewed as a measure of the genetic component, the other as a measure of the environmental component, and the area as the final phenotype. It is clear that if one dimension is greatly reduced (either the genetic or the environmental) the field will consist of a long strip of land with greatly reduced area. It is not possible to compensate effectively for a drastic reduction in one dimension by extending the other. On the other hand, it does not really matter whether the field is exactly square, or rectangular with a greater genetic or environmental dimension. The statement that intelligence in man is not inherited is absurd because without genes there would be no brain at all. Similarly absurd is the belief that intelligence is mainly determined by heritable factors. An individual brought up without any knowledge of language, or training of any kind, can hardly be expected to achieve his full intellectual potential.

The controversy is really about the extent to which genetic or environmental factors contribute to the variation between individuals. Situations are examined where the genetic factors are constant (as in identical twins) and the environment is varied (as in separated identical twins), or when the environment is *assumed* to be constant and there is genetic variation. The controversy is at present largely sterile, but that does not mean that it is not of vital importance properly to understand the forces that govern the interaction between the genotype and all the social, cultural, or other environmental influences. This is a theme which will recur frequently in the following sections, in which I shall consider in turn several areas of human behaviour or activity, which I believe will eventually come within the compass of exact knowledge.

One important question about early development concerns the nature of the interaction between infant and adult(s). At one extreme a child may be brought up entirely by its own mother and father, and at the other it may find itself in a totally communal system, where many adults participate in the upbringing and parents are not identifiable. In between there is a spectrum of possible situations in which grand-parents, foster mothers, professional child-minders, and so on, play the most active role. It is not known for certain which of these possible situations provides the ideal environment, which an adequate environment, and which might be positively deleterious; or whether several of the situations are equally satisfactory. It is also not known at which ages the child is most susceptible to adult influences. Many young animals 'imprint' the image of their mother at a particular period in their early development.[8] If another moving object is substituted for the parent at this time, the young animal imprints on this and there are subsequently profound consequences on the behaviour of the adult animal, for example, its sexual behaviour. The time and degree of importance of imprinting in the human infant is not known in any detail. It will be necessary to obtain unambiguous information about the way the young child actually establishes relationships with adults and what effects these relationships may have on subsequent development. When this information is gained, it will be of greatest importance in planning family lives and in avoiding situations which may have harmful later effects. Another vital component in development is the need for children to be in the company of other children with whom they can play or communicate their newly found experiences. Again, I suspect that the information we have at present is peripheral; much more exact knowledge is needed about the importance of their social life and the nature of the shared activities of children of all ages. As I said earlier some of this knowledge may come from observations similar to those made on social behaviour in animals, but a more profound understanding will depend on studies of the development of sensory perception and the way visual or other stimuli mould subsequent behaviour.

At a later stage, learning and education become dominant factors in the child's development. It is scarcely necessary to point out the wide areas of disagreement which exist at present among politicians, educational psychologists, teachers, and parents about the potential benefits, or otherwise, of different schooling systems. Everyone has their own opinions, but the real situation is that we do not actually know the relative merits of an educational environment where all the children participate on a more or less equal basis, as opposed to one where the children are separated according to differences in their ability to learn. When so little is known about the physiological process of learning, or the way interest and curiosity is actually generated and sustained, it is really impossible at present to do other than make intelligent guesses about the optimal educational environment and the methods of teaching which should be employed. Of course, educational psychologists are accumulating information all the time, but their approach is necessarily limited and a much more fundamental biological understanding of the process of learning and memory in man will eventually be essential to provide optimal environments for transmitting information to children.

As well as education *per se*, there is the equally important problem of the transition from childhood to adult. No one could claim that we really understand the origin of the antisocial, or antiparental, attitudes which frequently arise in adolescence. Little is known about the environmental factors which enhance it or diminish it, or whether, for instance, it is harmful or beneficial for the adolescent in question to go through such a stage prior to adulthood. The behaviour patterns of adolescents undoubtedly vary between societies; in some there appears to be very little change from generation to generation, whereas in others there is violent fluctuation from one generation to the next. There is certainly a great need to identify those factors which have harmful and those which have beneficial effects on the period of transition from childhood to adulthood.

I mentioned earlier that the very similar ability of men and women was well documented, but it would be surprising if their different biological roles in human reproduction did not also affect their aptitudes and potential in a variety of situations. At present this is a contentious area, because the social and environmental forces which differentially affect the behaviour of each sex are so complex. It would be extremely desirable to have the information which would enable individuals of each sex to fulfil better their potential and to strike the right balance between commitments to reproduction and family and commitments to other roles in society.

At present there is no concrete information about the origin of homosexual behaviour. E. O. Wilson has argued that there may be genetic factors predisposing people to become homosexual,[6] but a much more common view is that environmental influences are all-important. One very interesting possibility is that the environmental agent is teratogenic, that is, it operates during foetal development. K. Dorner has provided evidence that homosexuality may be the result of an abnormal sex-hormone balance during pregnancy, and the part of the brain determining maleness or femaleness may then be altered irreversibly.[9] It is possible that stressful situations produce the hormone imbalance, since a significantly greater proportion of children born in Germany during the last war became homosexual than those born six years afterwards or six years before. This requires much more investigation, since positive information could be acted upon, by heterosexual parents who want to avoid having homosexual children.

Man's willingness to resort to acts of violence is evident everywhere. Three general categories of violent or aggressive behaviour can be discerned. First, the violence of individuals within relatively stable communities in which the vast majority of people are non-violent. Second, violence which exists in mixed communities containing people belonging to different races or religions, or, in the case of violent revolution, to different political groups. Third, the general category of war, which is violent conflict between geographically separated communities.

So far as we know all these forms of violence have existed throughout man's history, but science and technology have enormously increased the scale of the problems by providing such a wide variety of weaponry. We have finally reached the absurd situation where a highly evolved and intelligent species is capable of committing mass suicide, through global nuclear war. What would observers from outer space think of a species which had developed a highly complex and sophisticated culture, yet which contained within it the most efficient means for self-destruction? They would certainly find it a biologically intriguing situation, worthy of a full investigation by appropriate techniques of research. To do this they would not only have to study the communities of men, but also the biological properties of individual men. In the future man himself must assume the role of these observers from outer space. To prevent violence and aggression it is first necessary to understand why it takes the form it does. It is easy to speculate that it arose from hunting, in which weapons were first used, and that it then spread to the conflicts between competing hunter–gatherer communities. Since each of these would have contained many interrelated individuals, selection for aggressiveness could have been based on kin selection or 'inclusive fitness'. What we have to understand is why violence and aggression can extend to situations, such as the First World War, which are totally disadvantageous to all the communities which are involved. Also, how is it possible for a small group of men, or even one man, to lead a whole nation to a largely self-destructive war, as occurred in the Second World War? These events can of course be fully analysed in historical terms, but underlying any explanation at this level there is necessarily the more fundamental biological one. Again, how can we explain the fact that people today can live apparently normal lives and yet accept with apparent equanimity that the means exist for their annihilation? How can one and the same individual be perfectly peaceable in one community and show unrestrained brutality in an inter-communal conflict? How can he be in complete harmony with his own family group, but violently aggressive in an intra-communal conflict? Finally, there is the problem of the individual criminal who is violent within an otherwise peaceable community.

At present we have little idea of the relative importance of cultural and innate factors involved in aggressive behaviour, let alone what these factors might actually be. We can speculate that competitive sport is a form of sublimated aggression,[10] but we cannot say we really understand at all the basis of the widespread enthusiasm for this form of leisure activity. When all these aspects of the human behavioural phenotype are understood, it should become possible to devise the means to prevent aggression or channel it effectively into harmless or even socially beneficial pathways.

It is hard to escape the conclusion that political theories have strong biological undertones. One political view is based on the premise that people who are given essentially the same opportunities end up with very different capabilities. In other words, people vary in their intelligence, enterprise or ambition and this variation is at least in part genetically determined. This is taken to justify a social structure which is stratified or hierarchical, with a privileged group holding the most influential and powerful positions and less privileged groups carrying out more menial or routine tasks for the community. Although there may in principle be equality of opportunity, in practice there is always competition among people of differing ability and therefore each person obtains a position in society which is most fitting for that ability. This is, in effect, the right-wing political philosophy.

The left-wing view starts from a quite different premise, namely, that all individuals are quite similar in their potential ability, and that the position they finally obtain is due to cultural or social influences. Thus, in right-wing societies the privileged individuals who have influence and power gain their position through having the best educational opportunities, the necessary social connections, and so on. The underprivileged working class are kept in that position through the deprivation of opportunities for social advancement. The socialist alternative is to allow equal opportunities for everyone and the result will necessarily be a more egalitarian and democratic society. Most socialists would not accept that the different roles people play in the socialist society are due to innate differences in ability, but rather that the necessary division of labour depends on people's choices, for example, whether or not they decide to spend many years in vocational training.

As I have repeatedly emphasized, the nature of the interaction between genotype and environment is crucial. People who fervently adopt one political viewpoint are in fact making tacit assumptions about this interaction. They are making a biological judgement. An extreme case of this comes from the

Marxist viewpoint. Marxists believe that their interpretation of history is in itself scientific and the ways in which societies will evolve are an inevitable part of that history. Popper[11] and Monod[12] have in different ways made it clear that the Marxist interpretation of history cannot be regarded as a scientific theory, since it does not make precise predictions and can always be modified to account for any historical or political event. At best, it can be described as pseudoscientific. Dialectical materialists are supposed thoroughly to approve of all forms of scientific research. Nevertheless when an experimental science is in conflict with a Marxist interpretation then that area of research must be suppressed. This happened to the science of genetics in the Soviet Union: the pseudobiology of Marxism was incompatible with the scientific facts revealed by genetic experimentation, therefore the latter had to be eliminated or discredited.[13] Although the study of genetics has now been reinstated in the Soviet Union, there is still a widespread view that the genetics of man is irrelevant, since the benefits of the communist system override any differences there might be in inherited characteristics.[14] (The well-known Soviet geneticist, N. Dubinin has even gone so far as to suggest that man in the Soviet Union has undergone social evolution to a new 'sub-species', *Homo sapiens humanis*, owing to the exceptionally favourable environment in which he lives![14]) The assumption that genetic differences between people are irrelevant is, of course, as unjustified as the opposing view that hierarchical societies exist simply because there are innate differences in intelligence or ability amongst people.

The point I am making is that much political theory is based on guesses about the nature of man. It will be possible in the future to do better than that, as we shall have answers to crucial questions that can be asked about people's intrinsic abilities in different environmental situations. Or, to put it another way, each person will be in a better position to know the roles in society he could play and he will be able to choose that which is most suitable and satisfying for him.

Religion is ubiquitous in human communities. It may exist because man, being conscious of his origin and his future death, and of the world around him, is continually asking questions. Where do we come from, where will we go, how did the universe come to exist and so on? Religion provides answers to these questions, and to make them carry conviction a variety of supernatural beings or forces are invoked which are based on or associated with a historical mythology. Science of course does not in general attempt to answer these questions. It is not possible for scientists to say why the universe or the laws of physics exist. On the other hand science is continually making many 'why' questions irrelevant. From what we know about atomic structure, it is possible to understand the fact that there are only about one hundred chemical elements. It is possible to understand why biological structures are largely made up of a limited number of these elements. The evolution of organisms including man is explicable on the basis of the chemical and physical properties of these biological structures. There is no longer any need to invoke vitalistic or any other supernatural forces to explain the origin of man. The absence of any non-material component, and the intrinsic limitation of the life-span of his body, makes the concept of an afterlife unnecessary. Therefore scientific research has shown that a large proportion of the various answers religion provides to these 'why' questions is totally irrelevant. One might therefore think that the elaborate superstructure of dogma, myths, miracles, and legends would come tumbling down, but this is far from the truth. Even communist societies, which have rejected religion, have put in its place dogmatic political ideologies which have some of the characteristics of religion. Moreover, people everywhere seem to be extremely prone to accept the existence of supernatural or paranormal phenomena which apparently defy rational explanation. In an earlier chapter I mentioned examples of 'spoon-bending' and the ability of plants to respond to external stimuli. To these could be added an enormous number of popular beliefs or superstitions, but I will list only a few: astrology and horoscopes; various forms of extrasensory perception; reincarnation or communication with the dead; flying saucers or other manifestations of extraterrestrial life; poltergeists and ghosts; exorcism; innumerable non-medical or miraculous cures for disease; palmistry; and scientology. In many cases people accept the reality of these phenomena on the flimsiest of grounds—perhaps the account of an event by a single individual. Acceptance is often tied up with a rejection of science. Thus the phrases 'scientists are baffled by' or 'scientists are quite unable to explain' such and such a happening are used again and again. On the other hand it is amusing to note that there is very often an individual in the background who has used scientific measurement or methods to 'prove' the reality of one or other of these paranormal phenomena. The case of extrasensory perception (ESP) is an interesting one. A few years ago, it seemed to have gained the status of an exact science. Experiments carried out under controlled conditions appeared to provide positive evidence for the existence of ESP.[15] Since that time an enormous amount of effort has been spent in trying to confirm and further document these experiments, and so far as I am aware, all these results have been negative. No consistent and reproducible procedure has been found which can demonstrate beyond reasonable doubt the existence of ESP.

One crucial problem is clearly that of the assessment of evidence which I discussed in Chapter 2. Rigorous methods are necessary to establish the validity of scientific conclusions, but where the conclusions conflict with traditional views, the non-scientist can reject them as easily as he may accept some of the phenomena I have just mentioned, even though they have never stood up to critical examination by scientific methods. Indeed, in many cases people positively prefer to accept a viewpoint simply because it is non-scientific or, as they believe, beyond scientific explanation.

It becomes necessary to explain why individuals are so prone to accept various forms of religion and superstition. One view, favoured by sociobiologists, is that genetic factors are involved. During the time man was evolving there would have been a need for continual awareness of the existence of dangerous predators, or perhaps other environmental hazards. Men would have to be always on the alert and suspicious of their environment and it may well have been that those who were the most suspicious, who suspected danger even when it did not exist, were the fittest in the Darwinian sense. The step from extreme suspicion to superstition may be a short one, and once this step had occurred there could be an innate tendency to believe in a wide variety of non-existent objects or forces.

It is very important to understand man's propensity to accept conclusions on the basis of totally inadequate evidence. Gullibility leads to exploitation, by conventional religious leaders, by mystics or gurus, by politicians, by self-styled experts in various fields of medicine and so on. The most extreme and dangerous form of persuasion is seen in the techniques of brainwashing, which convert an individual from one life-style or set of beliefs to a totally different one.[16] The neurophysiological basis of these processes is of extreme interest and must in the future be fully understood. A biological explanation of the events which lead man to have fixed and dogmatic attitudes should make it much easier to prevent the adoption of these attitudes. This in turn will remove one cause of the strife between and within communities which at present is such a dominant feature of the world scene.

As well as his capacity to communicate by language, man is unique among animals in his artistic creativity. In Chapter 2 I pointed out that the success of scientists does not seem to depend on their understanding of the underlying philosophy of the scientific method. In an analogous manner, artists are successful through their skill and creative intuition; there is no rational or objective formula which defines a successful and appealing work of art. Two essential elements of art are first individual creativity and second communal participation and aesthetic appreciation. We do not yet understand the *biological* basis of either of these aspects of human behaviour, although thousands of books have been written on the nature of art and aesthetics. The criteria for excellence are hard to define and this is the reason why so many creative artists are largely ignored in their lifetime. Only 'the test of time' decides whether or not an artist is to be forgotten or adulated. The situation is perhaps worse in the twentieth century than in earlier periods, since all manner of new forms of artistic expression are being explored. This diversity may provide richness to the overall field in question, but it is also clear that modern art has lost orientation in the sense that criteria for excellence are now even harder to discern or define than they were in the past. We have a situation which can be easily exploited by charlatans of one kind or another and where the general public is frequently misled by critics who are supposed to be capable of artistic judgements. As a result, creative art has lost a great deal of credibility and the genuinely original painter, writer, or musician suffers in consequence.

The remedy for this, is to re-establish criteria for excellence, but this is far easier said than done. One way would be to know much more about the aesthetic sense. If we understood why people respond with excitement and enthusiasm to the work of recognized composers, writers, or painters we would then be in a position to make the distinction between genuinely creative and indifferent art. A great deal is already known about the physical basis of sensory perception, but a much fuller understanding of brain function will be required before aesthetic enjoyment is understood. This knowledge would not, of course, make the slightest difference to our subjective feeling about or our response to art, but I believe it will make it possible to be more objective about the quality of any given work of art. Many people will think this is impossible, because art is always subjective. Again, I invoke the perceptive observer from outer space who wished to study and understand man's behaviour. He would have to explain why people consistently respond to particular pieces of music, paintings, poems, and so on, and consistently ignore others. Some objective criteria would be involved in drawing his conclusions. In a like manner an understanding of the aesthetic sense will make it possible to replace intelligent guesses, or the mere airing of opinions, with a far more positive and accurate assessment of quality.

Such information can only have beneficial consequences. Instead of the present inefficient system of identifying genuine creative artists, by their surviving the 'test of time' it should be possible to spot talent early on in their careers. In this way the situation which has all too often existed in the past and still exists today will be avoided: artists will not have to spend their time struggling to earn a living, they could receive financial support from the society in which they live and be free to devote their energy to creative work. I am not suggesting that any future objective understanding of the biological basis of the creation and the response to art will necessarily have any beneficial effect on its quality, although this is a possibility which certainly cannot be ruled out.

I have suggested that there are a number of areas of human activity and behaviour about which we are, at present, very largely ignorant. We have some information and people have to do the best they can with this; there are necessarily differences of opinion, different political viewpoints and often bitter controversies. There are conflicts of interest which cannot be resolved. There are disagreements about the relative benefit of short- and long-term aims. Solutions to all these problems must become easier if more unequivocal information is available.

The areas of ignorance I have discussed above are only a selected sample. As I mentioned at the outset, it would be presumptuous to try and guess what kind of knowledge will be obtained. It may well be that little progress will be made in some fields I have referred to, but enormous insights into human social behaviour will come from the investigation of certain kinds of human activity which I have not even mentioned. My main thesis, which will be challenged, is that it is vitally important to obtain by scientific methods as much information as possible about the nature of man as quickly as possible. This information will not constrict human lives, but will help to liberate society from many of the problems which at present seem to be totally insoluble. Conflicts, arguments, and disagreements within and between societies stem from the very fact that it is at present possible to adopt one of many political, moral, economic, or religious postures. But how would the new information be used? Who would be in a position to propagate it and why should people accept it?

On-going conflicts do not often exist in the realm of science, because the argument can usually be settled by observations or tests which will distinguish between conflicting theories. As science penetrates into more and more areas of human activity, arguments will also be settled in like manner. The scientist will not be in any particular position of power; he will merely be the instrument who provides the necessary information. This information must of course be disseminated (hence my preoccupation in this book with the problem of communication between scientists and non-scientists), but I believe this can be done effectively without any need for the public to become profoundly knowledgeable about the underlying technicalities. The dissemination of information is followed by decision-making; in many cases it will become self-evident that a particular course of action should be followed. In others democratic choice may well be involved, but hardly under the guidance of politicians. No doubt politicians will always exist, but I predict that they may well in future argue more and more about less and less.

The concept of power itself will change. In the previous chapter I used the example of biomedicine to illustrate that decisions can be made in human societies without any formal democratic apparatus and without coercion or any loss of freedom. It would not be possible to attribute power to any particular person or group of people in this area of human activity. Moreover, the advances are made and accepted at an international rather than at a national level. My prediction is that a similar situation will emerge with regard to many of the basic problems of human behaviour which plague our societies today.

# 9. Recapitulation

If the ultimate aim of the whole of science is indeed, as I
believe, to clarify man's relationship to the universe, then
biology must be accorded a central position, since of all
disciplines it is the one that endeavours to go most
directly to the heart of the problems that must be resolved
before that of 'human nature' can be framed in other than
metaphysical terms.

Jaques Monod[1]

IT took about one million years, or fifty thousand generations,
for man to evolve from his primate ancestors and finally form
large complex communities with established cultural traditions.
It took approximately six thousand years before advanced
science and technology arose out of these traditions. If the
evolution of man is represented by one calendar year, then his
civilizations have existed for no more than two days and the
atomic and molecular age for about fifteen minutes. We do not
know whether advanced civilizations such as ours are likely to
survive, on this time scale, for another few minutes, a few hours,
or another year or so. (It is a sobering thought that cosmologists
who speculate about the likely probability of receiving signals
from a civilization in outer space can make reasonable esti-
mates about the numbers, distances, and ages of possible
habitable planets, but they have no means at all of estimating
the likely survival time of advanced civilizations.) There is no
doubt that we ourselves are at present in a very unstable state,
since for the first time man has developed the means to destroy
his civilizations by weapons of mass destruction. If global war
does occur, it would not be in the least surprising if any surviving communities came to the conclusion that the *whole*
development of science and technology had been a disastrous
mistake. We might well expect such communities to outlaw the
very practice of science itself and perhaps destroy all remaining
scientific books and journals. In a sense, the beginning of such
an attitude already exists at present: there is a strong feeling in
many quarters that certain branches of science are potentially
so dangerous that their further development should be halted.

This hostility, however, is directed largely towards the chemical and biological sciences, rather than the physical ones. People strongly resent the danger of proliferating chemical industries and the release of various toxic substances into the environment. They worry about biologists manipulating DNA or embryos. Although there is plenty of hostility to nuclear power and the reprocessing of nuclear fuels, the worst consequences of nuclear physics—the existence of weapons of mass destruction—seem to have become an accepted part of the world scene. There appears to be little hope of nuclear weapons being dismantled by voluntary agreement and most people seem to believe that sooner or later their destructive powers will be unleashed. This fatalism is itself a depressing comment on human nature.

One of the main purposes of this book is to suggest that there may be a way of ridding the world of nuclear weapons and converting our unstable civilization into a stable and long-lasting one. I suggest that the hope lies in biology, in particular, the biology of man. My view is that if we were able to understand fully the reasons why man is so prone to adopt aggressive and threatening postures, we might be in a far better position to find the recipe to eliminate these postures—together with all the associated nuclear hardware.

Let me now recapitulate the general argument I have put forward. The synergistic interaction between genetics, biochemistry, and biophysics gave rise to the field of research known as molecular biology. Research in that field has been extraordinarily rapid since the early 1950s and has revealed both the basic molecular composition of living cells and the way in which macromolecules (DNA, RNA, and proteins) are synthesized and carry out their various biological functions. The genetic code turns out to be surprisingly simple and it is essentially the same in all organisms. The cracking of the code is probably the most important single achievement in science in this century, but overall, the most important success of molecular biology is to show that the properties of organisms are explicable in terms of physics and chemistry. Vitalistic or animistic forces have been expelled by the acquisition of exact knowledge. The near-universality of the code shows that all organisms evolved from a common primordial ancestor, and it follows from this they must share the same molecular building-blocks, which has in fact been demonstrated. The extreme external diversity of size, shape, and form of animals and plants, is a result of adaptations to all possible environments by Darwinian natural selection. In every case the adaptation provides the means for transmitting genetic information, the DNA of that species, from one generation to the next. All the studies which have been carried out on the biology of man, whether in genetics, biochemistry, or cell biology, show that he functions in the same way as other advanced organisms. (Indeed in biochemical terms, man is more closely related to a primate such as the chimpanzee, than two different species of *Drosophila* fruit flies are to each other.[2]) We certainly do not have a complete description of the molecular architecture of the human body, but there is no basis for the view that all its properties will not eventually be explicable in terms of physics and chemistry.

The methods and techniques of molecular biology have proved themselves to be by far the most successful within the whole field of biological research; there is every reason to believe that they will continue to advance our knowledge of biological systems indefinitely, provided, of course, that research in molecular biology receives sufficient financial and other support. This critically depends on the realization that the advance of biology is important and will be beneficial. If this science is to be accepted by the public at large, the channels of communication between scientists and non-scientists must be improved. Far too often people are just unaware of the significance of what has been going on in the laboratories of the molecular biologists. Even worse, they may simply disbelieve that the unravelling of the nature of life at the molecular level could be possible. I included a chapter on the success of the scientific method to try and explain how scientific advances are made. I pointed out that the firmness of a conclusion depends on the weight of experimental evidence in its favour; the problem for the non-scientist is that he is simply not aware of the experimental evidence and so can not accept the conclusion. There is no easy solution to this problem. It certainly helps if non-scientists adopt a rational attitude to science, and come to accept the fact that it is an extraordinarily successful means of obtaining new information about the world. This makes it harder to reject conclusions they simply do not want to believe (for example, that evolution occurs by natural selection or that all organisms are made up of molecules). It would also help if scientists took more time and trouble to explain their work in easily understood terms. More than fifty years ago J. B. S. Haldane, a leading biologist of his generation, wrote:

Many scientific workers believe that they should confine their publications to learned journals. I think, however, that the public has a right to know what is going on inside laboratories, for some of which it pays. And it seems to me vitally important that the scientific point of view should be applied, as far as possible, to politics and religion.[3]

Haldane put into practice this point of view since he subsequently wrote innumerable articles for non-scientists and several of his contemporaries also assumed that the interested public should be kept informed about current advances in science. Unfortunately this situation has since changed; most scientists now confine their publications to learned journals and communication between them and non-scientists is far less successful than it used to be. It is very important for scientists to understand that this puts them in a bad light and can lead to loss of support by the public.

Returning to the further advance of biological research, the first challenge in the future is to understand the process of development of higher organisms from the fertilized egg to adult. Our ignorance of this process is still profound, but there is no reason to suppose that appropriate experimental procedures will not be developed to answer the critical questions: the control of gene expression; the pathways of communication between cells; the forces which determine the shape of different parts of an organism; and so on. A complete description of simple multicellular organisms will be followed, step by step, by more and more understanding of complex ones.

An even greater challenge for future biology is to understand the structure and function of the central nervous system. Its particular feature is the extremely high degree of specificity which controls the way neurones make connections with each other. The exact nature of this specificity is not yet known, but it will almost certainly be first revealed by the study of the nervous system of simple animals. This breakthrough will then be followed by the analysis and understanding of the more complex systems of higher organisms. The brain of an animal is certainly its most complex component and it is the last we shall understand. Over and above that, there is the final challenge to biologists: an understanding of the function of the human brain. I do not accept the view that there are defined limits to biological research and that the unravelling of human brain function is beyond this limit. On the contrary, I have suggested earlier on that there are several reasons for believing that we shall achieve this understanding, although the necessary research may occupy biologists for a very long time to come. It could be maintained that the human brain is so complex that no one man could ever comprehend its function. That may well be so, but we could probably make the same statement about the whole of biology, or nuclear physics. It does not mean that an overall knowledge cannot exist, but only that the knowledge may have to be shared between several or many people.

Any complete scientific understanding of man will necessarily include an understanding of his behaviour. Since behaviour is the result of a complex interaction between genetic make-up and environmental influences, a complete description will require a knowledge of all the external forces which shape the emotional and intellectual development of human beings. Most of the human or social sciences today deal, in one way or another, with these external forces. Also, the greatest figures in literature owe their fame and influence to their unique insight into the way people actually behave and relate to each other under particular circumstances. The whole literary tradition provides a solid body of information about man, as does, in a totally different way, research in the fields of psychology, social anthropology, sociology, and related areas. Nevertheless, all these diverse studies of man cannot alone be expected to explain the basis of human behaviour, but eventually the information will complement that which will come from cell and molecular biology, or neurobiology, and this will lead to a complete synthesis.

The many problems which beset human societies stem from ignorance. Everywhere we see people expressing firm opinions in politics, in education, in religion, in art, or about 'human nature'. The strength of an opinion does not relate at all to the information available: it is based, at best, on intelligent guesswork and, at worst, on blind faith or dogma. In any human society, ethical judgements are continually being made. Often, of course, the ethical code has been decided long ago by religious prophets, who have given it permanence by invoking divine guidance or revelation. It is then transmitted from generation to generation in more or less unaltered form. In other cases, ethical judgements may be entirely secular; they 'emerge' in a society for reasons which are sometimes hard to discern and they may change rapidly in the space of a generation. Attitudes to sexual behaviour provide a clear example. Sociobiologists argue that the roots of ethical behaviour are to be found in an understanding of the evolution of aggression, altruism, sexual habits, and families or larger kin groups during man's emergence from his primate ancestors. Whichever way we think about the origins of an ethical system, we cannot escape the fact that it is an imperfect improvisation. It could hardly be otherwise, since different human societies have different ethical codes and all cannot provide the perfect answers. It is a depressing aspect of human behaviour itself that the members of each closely knit social, political, or religious group too often firmly believe that they have developed the ideal ethical system and exclude the possibility that alternatives might be just as satisfactory.

The major misconception, however, is that science is totally outside this realm of human activity. It is felt that ethical judgements must be based on an inner conscience, or be guided by religion, or come from democratic decisions, and that this situation will never change. If science comes at all into the process of choosing between one course of action or another, it is only to help provide a 'scientific attitude', that is, a proper assessment of all the information available and a rational decision about what should be done. Governments sometimes appoint scientific advisors, because it is felt that their opinions might in some cases be more valuable than those of non-scientists. Yet, as most people know, individual scientists are just as likely to be prejudiced or biased as anyone else in areas outside their own field of study.

The misconception is due in part to a confusion between what science as a whole can provide and the way in which individual scientists, in positions of influence or authority, may actually behave. The crucial point is that when science provides the relevant information it can, at least in principle, be disseminated to the public at large. It is the responsibility of the scientist to explain to the public what they are doing in their laboratories and it is necessary for non-scientists to understand fully how scientific research advances and to be able to distinguish between genuine findings and spurious claims. When information is made available it may then be ignored, as in the case of the health hazard of cigarette smoking, but more often it is noted and acted upon. It often becomes self-evident that a particular course of action should be followed and no elaborate machinery for decision-making (democratic or otherwise) need be set up. I illustrated this with examples from biomedicine in Chapter 7; the examples necessarily had to come from medicine because this is the area of human biology which so far has had the main impact on societies. This impact does not come from coercion; individual experts certainly do not bully, or even persuade, an unwilling public to undertake a particular course of action. What happens is that the information is gradually disseminated, since, as I pointed out, the communication between the medical profession and the public is fairly good. Once the information is available it is acted on by people who may be entirely ignorant of the underlying scientific research which was, in the first place, instrumental in providing the information. Under these circumstances sensible and rational decisions are made and there is usually a welcome absence of contentious argument. We do not often find that a society is divided into two or more camps each advocating a particular course of action. Nor is there any formal democratic procedure involved: there may be a choice between alternatives, but in most cases the correct choice is so obvious that there can be no disagreement about it. It is almost as if people are being overtaken by events, without being aware of it. No one is manipulating their lives; but their lives, as a result of their own free decisions, are being changed in all kinds of ways and these changes, much more often than not, are beneficial and life enhancing.

In future this will happen in more and more areas of human activity. As areas of ignorance are filled up one by one, the possibilities of dispute and of uncertainty will gradually decrease. We have already seen in the last hundred years or so a retreat of religious leaders from positions of power and influence in the United Kingdom and this was in large part due to the Darwinian revolution in biology. Yet the scale of this retreat would have been unthinkable, say, one hundred and fifty years ago, let alone in earlier periods of history. In the same way I believe that the power and influence of political figures will decline in the future, although to most people this is also unthinkable. I believe their importance will decline because more and more decisions will in effect be taken out of their hands. Their power will be taken out of their hands by the public itself, not directly, of course, by the scientists.

This brings me to the vital issue which I have not previously emphasized and this is the *urgency* of pursuing the study of human biology. We are confronted with a race between the continuing development of a potentially self-destructive technology and the advance of the scientific understanding of the basis of human behaviour. It is therefore tragic that fundamental or basic research is nowadays regarded as something of a luxury. The common view is that a few of the best scientists should be encouraged to break new ground. They should be given support and the freedom to pursue their own interests, but the majority of scientists should be employed to pursue defined, relatively short-term projects which can be expected to produce practical benefits in the fairly near future. This distinction between the roles different scientists should play in society is short-sighted and mistaken. In comparison to the enormous sums of money which have been spent on nuclear physics and which are still being spent on military research and development, the amount made available to biologists in universities and institutes is trivial. Fundamental biological research is not very expensive and it could be enormously expanded. Francis Crick has argued that it would be far better if the USA and the USSR competed in a *knowledge race* rather than an arms race.[4] Who could possibly disagree with that? It is, of course, not only a question of the training of scientists and the provision of laboratories and facilities for research. It is also essential for scientists themselves to have an optimistic view; to feel that they have it in their power to accumulate in the future a body of knowledge which will not only be beneficial, but vital for the future well-being of socieites. However humble their role may appear to be in the day-to-day work in a laboratory lacking glamour or fame, they should realize that they are, in one way or another, contributing to this knowledge.

I am not ignoring all the difficulties which lie ahead, even if the scientific advances I have mentioned do take place. For example, how do we balance a short-term benefit for a community against the possibility of a long-term one? Or why should we be concerned at all about what happens to future generations? There are two basic features of the biological species *Homo sapiens*: first, he successfully transmits his genes from generation to generation, just as any other surviving species does; but, in addition, he has the second unique feature of cultural transmission. Information of all kinds, as well as skills, crafts, arts, language, myths, traditions, and so on, are passed down from generation to generation. In his book *The selfish gene*, Richard Dawkins invents a new word the *meme*, which he defines as any cultural item or feature which is transmitted in a manner analogous to the transmission of genes.[5] All advanced cultures take great care to transmit information, or memes, to future generations. Scientists are in a privileged position because they are accumulating knowledge of all kinds which is documented and stored away in innumerable scientific journals and books in libraries all around the world. (They could be referred to as meme banks.) It is particularly satisfying for a scientist to witness the spread of new information or ideas which are the result of his own hard work or his own creative imagination. The same applies to any creative artist whose work is destined to survive for the benefit of future generations. We can invoke the term *superconscious*. The body dies, but the products of the mind survive and influence further generations. The concept of a superconscious could easily replace the religious myth of an immortal soul. Most people reproduce and transmit their own genes, parents and teachers transmit existing knowledge, but the creation and transmission of new knowledge is at the present time largely in the hands of the scientists, since they are continually obtaining most of the new information. There is plenty of evidence that man has an intrinsic urge to expand his knowledge and to hand it down to later generations, otherwise we could hardly have evolved complex societies. This then provides the answer to the question about long-term aims and the well-being of future generations. The future will be well taken care of, provided, of course, that our civilization does not destroy itself first.

Six thousand years of political manoeuvre, of religious dogma, of diplomacy and war, have provided no lasting solutions to the major problems facing mankind. Whichever way we consider them, these problems are ultimately biological ones. I believe the answers will only be forthcoming by using the revolutionary studies in molecular biology as a foundation for the further pursuit of biological research at all levels, which will finally lead to the knowledge we need of man himself.

# References and notes

## Preface

1. Crick, F. H. C. *Molecules and men*, University of Washington Press, Seattle (1966).
2. Monod, J. *Chance and necessity*, Collins, London (1972, translated from *Le hazard et la necessité*, Editions du Seuil, Paris (1970).
3. Medawar, P. B. *The art of the soluble*, Methuen, London (1967).
4. Medawar, P. B. *The hope of progress*, Methuen, London (1972).

I use the term 'scientist' to describe anyone who is professionally trained to carry out research or to teach science. A non-scientist or layman would be anyone without formal scientific training who has an interest in, or at least an awareness of, the practice of science. Throughout the book I use, for brevity, only the male pronouns; in all cases this refers to male or female individuals. In the same way, K. R. Popper's use of the term 'thinking man' (in the quotation on page 9) obviously applies to individuals of either sex.

## Chapter 1

1. Medawar, P. B. *The hope of progress*, page 103, Methuen, London (1972).
2. Wilson, E. O. *Sociobiology*, Harvard University Press, Cambridge, Mass. (1975).
3. Crick, F. H. C. *Molecules and men*, page 94, University of Washington Press, Seattle (1966).

## Chapter 2

1. Popper, K. R. *The logic of scientific discovery*, Preface to first edition, Hutchinson, London (1959).
2. Medawar, P. B. *Induction and intuition in scientific thought*, Methuen, London (1969).
3. Gregor Mendel's classical paper has been translated many times. A recent English version can be found in *The origins of genetics: a Mendel source book* (Edited by C. Stern and E. R. Sherwood), W. H. Freeman, San Francisco (1966).
4. The detailed and exact calculations which are necessary for all travel in space, for landing men on the moon or instruments on Mars, are based on Newton's laws of gravity and motion.
5. Whitehorn, K. A case of nobelesse O'Blige. *The Observer* (London) 9 March 1980.

6. For example, Arthur Koestler has consistently ignored the experimental and theoretical basis for Darwinian evolution by natural selection and instead advocated the Lamarckian inheritance of acquired characteristics, for which there is neither experimental evidence nor any theoretical basis. See *The ghost in the machine*, Hutchinson, London (1967); *The case of the midwife toad*, Hutchinson, London (1971); *Janus: A summing up*, Hutchinson, London (1978). See also, Chapter 6, page 65 and reference 4.

7. Bose, C. J. *Physiology of the ascent of sap*. Longmans, London (1923). A contemporary discussion of Bose's claim to have discovered animal-like rhythms in plants can be found in H. H. Dixon's *The transpiration stream*, University of London Press (1924).

8. Tomkins, P. and Bird, C. *The secret life of plants*, Allen Lane, London (1974).

9. Popper, K. R. *The logic of scientific discovery*, Hutchinson, London (1972). A clear exposition of Popper's philosophical work has been written by B. Magee: *Popper*, Fontana and Collins, Glasgow (1973).

A very readable review of the philosophy of science, including an assessment of the contributions of K. R. Popper and T. Kuhn, has been written by A. F. Chalmers: *What is this thing called science?* The Open University Press, Milton Keynes (1976).

## Chapter 3

1. Crick, F. H. C. *Molecules and men*, page 10, University of Washington Press, Seattle (1966).

The most comprehensive and up-to-date review of molecular biology is J. D. Watson's *Molecular biology of the gene*, 3rd Edition, W. A. Benjamin, California (1977). A more readable, but less up-to-date account, can be found in J. C. Kendrew's *Thread of life*, Harvard University Press, Cambridge, Mass. (1966).

2. Garrod, A. E. *Inborn errors of metabolism* (2nd edn), Hodder & Stoughton, London (1923).

3. Schrödinger, E. *What is life?* Cambridge University Press (1944).

4. A popular and illuminating account of the events leading up to this discovery can be found in J. D. Watson's *The double helix*, Weidenfeld & Nicolson, London (1968).

5. Holliday, R. Should the genetic engineers be contained? *New Scientist*, p. 399, February (1977). I defined the term *heterogenetics* as follows: the synthesis and study of replicating DNA molecules containing nucleotide sequences from unrelated organisms.

## Chapter 4

1. Crick, F. H. C. *Molecules and men*, pages 8 and 93, University of Washington Press, Seattle (1966).

The best modern account of evolution by natural selection is by J. Maynard Smith: *The theory of evolution* (3rd edn), Penguin, Harmondsworth, Middx (1975).
2. Orgel, L. E. *The origins of life*, Chapman and Hall, London (1973).
3. Orgel, L. E. Selection *in vitro*. In *The evolution of adaptation by natural selection* (Edited by J. Maynard Smith and R. Holliday). *Proc. R. Soc., B.*, p. 435, London (1979).
4. Maynard Smith, J. *The evolution of sex*, Cambridge University Press (1976).
5. Dawkins, R. *The selfish gene*, Oxford University Press (1976).
6. For a discussion of the evolution of the innate ability to learn language, see J. Monod *Chance and necessity*, Collins, London (1972).
7. Wilson, E. O. *On human nature*, page 2, Harvard University Press, Cambridge, Mass. (1978).
8. See, for example, M. J. Lamb's *The biology of ageing*, pp. 143–162. Blackie, Glasgow (1977).
9. Wilson, E. O. *Sociobiology*, Harvard University Press, Cambridge, Mass. (1975).

## Chapter 5

1. Medawar, P. B. *The hope of progress*, page 124, Methuen, London (1972).
2. Dreisch, H. *The science and philosophy of the organism* (2 vols.) Adam and Charles Black, London (1908).
3. Crick, F. H. C. *Molecules and men*, page 64, University of Washington Press, Seattle (1966).
4. McKusick, V. A. *Mendelian inheritance in man* (4th edn), Johns Hopkins University Press (1978).
5. Darwin, C. *The expression of the emotions in man and animals*, J. Murray, London (1872).
6. See, for example, D. Morris *The naked ape*, Cape, London (1967); *The human zoo*, Cape, London (1969); K. Lorenz, *On aggression*, Methuen, London (1966).

Non-ethologists have also extrapolated studies of animal behaviour to the interpretation of human behaviour; for example, L. Tiger and R. Fox *The imperial animal*, Holt, Rinehart, and Winston, New York (1971) and R. Ardrey *The social contract*, Collins, London (1970).

## Chapter 6

1. Medawar, P. B. *The hope of progress*, page 127, Methuen, London (1972).
2. Pritchard, R. H. Recombinant DNA is safe. *Nature (Lond.)* **273**, 696 (1978).
3. Rorvik, D. M. *In his image: the cloning of a man*, Lipincott, Philadelphia (1978).
4. Shaw, G. B. Preface to *Back to Methuselah*, Constable, London (1921).

# Chapter 7

1. The subtitle to F. H. C. Crick's *Molecules and men* is 'Exact knowledge is the enemy of vitalism'. Similarly, it is the enemy of controversy. Exact knowledge cannot be defined in a way which would satisfy philosophers. My definition emerges from the discussion in Chapter 2. In effect, I use the term to describe any discovery which is beyond controversy. Thus, the circulation of the blood; the chemical composition of numerous inorganic or organic substances; the identity of many pathogens causing human diseases; and the make up of the genetic code, are all examples of exact knowledge.

2. Sutherland, N. S. *Breakdown*, Stein and Day, New York (1976).

3. Price, W. H., Brunton, M., Buckten, K., Jacobs, P. A. Chromosome survey of new patients admitted to four maximum security hospitals in the United Kingdom. *Clin. Genet.* **9**, 389 (1976).

# Chapter 8

1. Dobzhansky, Th. Anthropology and the natural sciences: the problem of human evolution. *Curr. Anthropol.* **4**, 146 (1963).

2. Popper, K. R. *Conjectures and refutations: the growth of scientific knowledge* (4th edn), page 37, Routledge & Kegan Paul, London (1972).

3. See, for example, F. R. Leavis *Education and the university*, Chatto and Windus, London (1943).

4. Sutherland, N. S. *Breakdown*, Stein and Day, New York (1976).

5. Wilson, E. O. *Sociobiology*, Harvard University Press, Cambridge, Mass. (1975).

6. Wilson, E. O. *On human nature*, Harvard University Press, Cambridge, Mass. (1978).

7. Gould, S. J. and Lewontin, R. C. The spandrels of San Marco and the Panglossian paradigm. In *The evolution of adaptation by natural selection* (Edited by J. Maynard Smith and R. Holliday) *Proc. R. Soc. B.* p. 581, London (1979).

8. Lorenz, K. Der Kumpan in der Umwelt des Vogels. *J. Ornith*, **83**, 137 and 289 (1935). Lorenz, K. *King Solomon's Ring*, Methuen, London (1952)

9. Dorner, G. Hormones and sexual differentiation of the brain. In *Sex hormones and behaviour*, CIBA Foundation Symposium 62, Excerpta Medica, Amsterdam (1979).

10. Lorenz, K. *On aggression*, Methuen, London (1966).

11. Popper, K. R. *The poverty of historicism*, Routledge & Kegan Paul, London (1957).

12. Monod, J. *Chance and necessity*, Collins, London (1972).

13. Medvedev, Zh. A. *The rise and fall of T. D. Lysenko*, Columbia University Press, New York (1969).

14. Medvedev, Zh. A. A new controversy in Soviet genetics, *Nature (Lond.)* **268**, 285 (1977).

15. See, for example, contributions to *Extrasensory perception* (Edited by G. E. W. Wolstenholme and E. C. P. Millar) CIBA Foundation Symposium, Churchill, London (1956).
16. Sargant, W. W. *Battle for the mind*, Heinemann, London (1957).

## Chapter 9

1. Monod, J. Preface to *Chance and necessity*, Collins, London (1972).
2. King, M.-C. and Wilson, A. C. Evolution at two levels in humans and chimpanzees. *Science, NY* **188**, 107 (1975).
3. Haldane, J. B. S. Preface to *Possible worlds and other essays*, Chatto and Windus, (London (1927).
4. Crick, F. H. C. *Molecules and men*, University of Washington Press, Seattle (1966).
5. Dawkins, R. *The selfish gene*, Oxford University Press (1976).

# Index